It's another great book from CGP...

This book is for anyone studying KS3 English (ages 11-14).

It contains lots of tricky questions designed to make you sweat —
with answers at the back so that you can check how you're getting on.

CGP — still the best! ☺

Our sole aim here at CGP is to produce the highest quality books —
carefully written, immaculately presented and dangerously close to being funny.

Then we work our socks off to get them out to you
— at the cheapest possible prices.

Contents

Section Six — Writing — The Basics

Section Seven — Paragraphs

Section Eight — Writing Properly

Section Nine — Making It Interesting

Section Ten — Writing Practice Questions

Published by CGP

Editors:
Emma Bonney
David Broadbent
Sabrina Robinson

With thanks to Anthony Muller for the proofreading.
With thanks to Laura Jakubowski for the copyright research.

Extract from *The Sea Raiders* by H.G. Wells on p.22 reprinted by permission of United Agents on behalf of: The Literary Executors of the Estate of H.G. Wells

ISBN: 978 1 84762 258 7

Clipart from Corel®
Printed and bound by Bell & Bain Ltd, Glasgow.

Based on the classic CGP style created by Richard Parsons.

Audience

Authors write differently for different audiences. You need to be able to spot who the audience is when you're reading a text — and think about your audience when doing your own writing.

Q1 Texts A-D have been written for different types of reader or audience. Match up each text with its intended reader or audience (**i-iv**).

A Last week, a local schoolboy got more than he bargained for when he added his mother's rhubarb crumble to a tank of algae. The result of this bizarre experiment? A teacher described it in one word: "Mayhem." The boy, aged 13, cannot be named for legal reasons.

B Last week, I did a really interesting experiment in my school. I tried adding rhubarb crumble to a tank of algae. Do you know what algae is? It's a sort of moss that grows on the surface of ponds. After three days, I found that the algae was growing bigger and bigger.

C Did I tell you that I did an amazing experiment in school last week? We were adding different things to tanks of algae to see what would happen. I added my mum's rhubarb crumble. Well, that was a mistake! The algae grew absolutely enormous; it was bigger than Gavin's bike.

D My teacher suggested that I should describe my algae experiment to you, in the hope that you could shed some light on the results. The algae was from a pond in Haverthwaite. About 50 cm³ was used in a 5 litre tank of water. One standard portion of crumble was added.

i) A friend C ✓   **ii)** Readers of a local newspaper B A ✓   **iii)** An expert B ✓   **iv)** Pupils of a local primary school B ✓

4/4

Q2 Write a sentence explaining why each of the texts suits the reader or audience you chose in **Q1**. Think about the vocabulary and style used.

In A it is written like a newspaper. In B it is I says I so it would be to Pupils of a local Primary school. In c it starts with did it tell you. In d it has a lot of complicated language ✓

3/4

Q3 Match sentences **a)-c)** below with the correct audience from the box.

a) Ladies and Gentlemen, Mr Chairperson, esteemed guests — I bid you the warmest of welcomes on this very special evening. ✓

b) Timmy, the teeny-weeny caterpillar, was very sad. None of his friends wanted to play with him, not even Matthew the Mole.

c) Please respect others and their belongings, and keep your uniform smart at all times. ✓

school pupils
toddlers
adults

3/3

Purpose

Everything you read has a purpose — even this bit of text. Make sure you can recognise the most common types and how they affect the style of a text.

Q1 a) Match up each piece of writing A-D with its purpose (**i-iv**).

A *Log Book of Professor Andrea Miller*
2ⁿᵈ February 2014
Breakthrough — there's a reason why the penguin robots are malfunctioning! It's because running them on fish oil is playing havoc with their electrical systems. I'm going to try them on motor oil from tomorrow.

B The threat that these robot penguins pose to the nation is clear. They are unpredictable, uncontrollable and unnatural. Surely, ladies and gentleman, we all agree that the best thing to do is to destroy them?

C Miller and Danthorpe listened, still as shadows. A low buzzing sound was coming from the robot. The professors began to slowly edge their way towards the door at the other end of the laboratory. As Professor Miller's hand grasped the door knob, she felt a cold metal flipper on her shoulder...

D The 'Miller and Danthorpe Epidemic of Unnatural Penguins' occurred in 2014 when two little-known professors at the University of Beanthwaite attempted to create robotic penguin assistants. Unfortunately, the resulting robots proved impossible to control. Official statistics state that there were 5024 injuries caused by the robots. The two professors were never found.

i)   To inform D ✓ ii)   To entertain C ✓ iii)   To argue or persuade B ✓ iv)   To explain

A ✓

b) Explain briefly why you chose your answers in part **a)**.

Text A gives reasons. text B says positive and negative factors. ✓
text gives us some sun and action. text states lots of facts. ✓ 3/4

Q2 The purpose of the passage below is to inform.
Rewrite the passage, making its purpose to argue or persuade.

> There are currently around 34 million hens in the UK that are laying eggs for human consumption. The demand for eggs has meant that 16 million of these hens are kept in small cages. These cages are usually stacked on top of each other indoors, and are often shared between three or four birds.
>
> Most of the remaining 18 million hens are 'free range'. These hens have continuous access to outdoor space which they can roam freely. Some people choose to eat only free range eggs, even though they're more expensive than eggs from caged hens. Studies have shown that there are higher quantities of nutrients in eggs from free range hens.

Robotic penguins — sounds flipper-ing dangerous...
Always think about purpose when you're reading a text — it'll help you to understand it.

Context

You don't need to know the author's whole life story (some of them are mighty dull). However, context does have a big impact on a text, so it's a good idea to practise writing about it.

Q1   The passage below is taken from *Persuasion* by Jane Austen:

> "You know," said she, "I cannot think him at all a good match for Henrietta; and considering the alliances which the Musgroves have made, she has no right to throw herself away. I do not think any young woman has a right to make a choice that might be disagreeable and inconvenient to the principal part of her family, and be giving bad connections to those who have not been used to them. And, pray, who is Charles Hayter? Nothing but a country curate. A most improper match for Miss Musgrove of Uppercross."

a)   What does this extract suggest to you about the main purpose of marriage among the upper classes in Jane Austen's time?

b)   What impression do you get about the role of young women in society at that time?

Q2   The extract below is from Wilfred Owen's First World War poem *Dulce Et Decorum Est*.

> Men marched asleep. Many had lost their boots
> But limped on, blood-shod. All went lame; all blind;
> Drunk with fatigue; deaf even to the hoots
> Of tired, outstripped **Five-Nines** that dropped behind.
>
> GAS! GAS! Quick, boys! — An ecstasy of fumbling,
> Fitting the clumsy helmets just in time;
> But someone still was yelling out and stumbling,
> And flound'ring like a man in fire or lime...
> Dim, through the misty panes and thick green light,
> As under a green sea, I saw him drowning.
>
> In all my dreams, before my helpless sight,
> He plunges at me, guttering, choking, drowning.

Five-Nines — 5.9-inch calibre shells

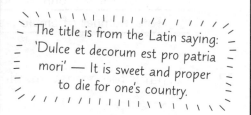

The title is from the Latin saying: 'Dulce et decorum est pro patria mori' — It is sweet and proper to die for one's country.

a)   What does this poem tell you about the conditions endured by soldiers during the First World War? Use quotes from the text to back up each point you make.

b)   How does the author show his personal feelings about the war?

c)   What does the end of the poem (below) suggest to you about the attitude of society towards war at that time?

Hint: look for parts that are written in the first person.

> My friend, you would not tell with such high zest
> To children ardent for some desperate glory,
> The old Lie: Dulce et decorum est
> Pro patria mori.

Finding the Important Bits

To answer reading questions it will really help if you find the key words and phrases in the text. Just find the right bit and then write it down — it's not too tricky. Not too tricky at all.

An extract from a magazine article about the PB Animation Studio

The PB Animation Studio was founded in 1998 by Managing Director Paul Black, and since then it has become a hugely successful business. In the beginning, it was just Paul working alone in his attic room, but now the company employs 230 people in jobs ranging from scriptwriters to cooks!

The secret of PB's success has always been the quality of its 3D animation. Characters are carefully shaped from ordinary modelling clay, and are usually no more than 20 centimetres tall. More complex characters have wire frames (or rod-and-joint structures called armatures) inside the clay. These allow the model to be adjusted very accurately.

The really time-consuming part of the job is actually filming — in order for the characters' movements to appear realistic, 24 pictures (or 'frames') need to be taken to put together 1 second of finished film!

Q1 Copy and complete the table using information from the magazine article above.

Description	Fact
Year PB Animation Studio was created	*in 1998*
Founded by...	*Paul Black*
Paul Black's current position	*employs 230 people*
Total number of employees today	*230*

Q2 What is the normal maximum height of PB's characters?

Usually no more than 20cm

Q3 What must be included in models that need very accurate adjustment?

They would have wired frames

Q4 What are 'armatures'?

rod-and-joint structures (wire frames)

Q5 How many frames per second need to be filmed? Choose from options i)-iv).

i) 20   **ii)** 230   **iii)** 24   **iv)** 25

You don't need to write loads — just write out the bit of the text that answers the question.

Q6 Why is this number of frames per second needed?

To make the movements look realistic

Q7 According to the writer, what is the secret of PB's success?

the quality of it's 3D animations

Finding the Important Bits

Here's some more practice at digging out the juicy bits in texts. Remember — you're looking for the bits that help you to answer the question. So jot those bits down and forget the rest.

An extract from the story *Carrie's Life of Piracy*

Carrie darted round the corner into a dingy side-street full of discarded wooden crates. She was closely followed by Ben, who stopped and bent over, panting. He felt like he'd been out of breath ever since they'd left the Pirate Academy.

"Come on, Ben! We have to keep moving — otherwise they'll send us back, and you know what that means..."

Suddenly they were aware of a shadow looming over them. Carrie gasped and looked up towards the leering, cruel face of Captain Hack.

"My dear pupils," said Hack, relishing each word, "I'm only doing my duty as your tutor. You know that any student failing to hand in homework must walk the plank."

Carrie and Ben exchanged a glance. Ben dashed forward with a yell, and managed to slip between Captain Hack's legs. Before Hack could react, Ben ripped a thin plank of wood from a nearby crate.

"Catch!" he shouted, and tossed the plank over Hack's head, to be caught by Carrie.

For a moment Carrie looked at the plank, bemused. Then she remembered her sword-fighting lessons, and crouched with the plank in her hand, ready to defend herself against her pirate tutor.

Q8 Write out the part of the text where you are told about the following things.

a) Where Carrie and Ben arrive at the start of the extract.

b) How Ben feels at the beginning of the extract.

c) Where Carrie and Ben have come from.

d) What Captain Hack looks like.

e) How Captain Hack wants to punish Carrie and Ben.

f) What Carrie and Ben did that needs to be punished.

g) How Ben escapes from Captain Hack.

h) Where Ben got the thin plank of wood from.

Umm... I'd better head back. Reports to write, homework to mark...

Q9 How do Carrie and Ben know that Captain Hack has arrived?
Write out the part of the text that tells you.

Q10 What is Carrie about to do with the thin plank of wood?
Write out the part of the text that tells you.

Trapped in a snow poem — it was phrasing...
Finding the important bits quickly is a really useful skill and saves copying out huge chunks of text.

Summarising

If you're asked to summarise the points made in a text, it means that you need to write the important bits out <u>in your own words</u>. And don't waffle — summarise as briefly as possible.

An extract from the story *Felix and the Dragon's Revenge*

> The elderly King looked down his nose at the men assembled before him.
>
> "Do you mean to tell me that they *all* went free?" he thundered.
>
> Felix remained on his knees and let out a gentle sob. The King, becoming somewhat reflective, turned and gazed vacantly out of the tall window.
>
> "It wasn't always like this," he muttered. "During the reign of my father, captured knights had some respect and *stayed* captured. Aaah, what it was to be a child. I used to play in that very garden. Haha! The fun I had with my wooden horse... Ahem. Anyway, it just won't do, there have been too many daring escapes recently."
>
> Felix was about to interrupt, but the King's courtier placed a hand on his shoulder to stop him.
>
> "And you," began the King, his voiced raised and turning to face Felix, "You have done nothing to stop these knights!" He gestured to Prime Minister Katan. "Tie Felix up, take him to Vertis Ledge, and let the dragons do as they wish."
>
> As Felix was being dragged away by two burly attendants, he found the strength to cry out, "You'll see, my lord! One of these days the dragons will come after you!"

Q1   Make a list of all the characters mentioned in the text.

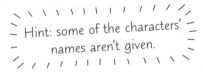
Hint: some of the characters' names aren't given.

Q2   Which of the characters actually speak in the text?

Q3 a) Copy out and correct this summary of the paragraph starting "It wasn't..."

The King remembers when his father ruled, and knights were harder to control. He decides that something must be done. Then he starts to think about his childhood when he played with his toys in the garden.

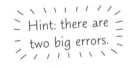
Hint: there are two big errors.

b) Copy out the sentence that describes the King's mood in the paragraph starting "It wasn't..."

i)   He seems angry with Felix, and keeps shouting at him.

ii) He seems angry with Felix, but is easily distracted by memories of his childhood.

iii) He talks about his childhood and doesn't care about the knights at all.

Q4   Summarise the paragraph starting "And you," in your own words.

Q5   Write a summary of the whole text. Your summary should be no more than five sentences long, and you'll have to decide which of the details on this page need to be included.

Working Out What's Going On

Not all texts are easy-peasy — some can be downright confusing. But don't panic — focus on working out what happens. A summary in your own words, or a numbered list, might help.

An extract from the short story *Mrs Hanrahan's Holiday*

Ever since she'd woken to shrill beeps that still echoed around her head, Mrs Hanrahan's day had got worse and worse. She'd had to spend a few hours hunting for the tickets — knowing that without them she *definitely* wouldn't be going on holiday today. She'd finally located the tickets beneath the tottering pile of dirty dishes, but hadn't retrieved them safely before sacrificing two of the dishes to the floor in a flurry of ceramic and congealed Chinese takeaway.

Finally, Mrs Hanrahan was ready.

"Bags packed – check. Tickets – check. House keys – check," she murmured. She placed the front door keys carefully on top of the tickets. With a grimace, Mrs Hanrahan suddenly remembered to put the milk bottles outside. She abandoned her luggage, collected the bottles, wrote a quick note to the milkman and then ventured outside. Just as she placed the bottles by the front doormat, Mrs Hanrahan was aware of the sound of the front door latch clicking behind her...

Q1 Copy and complete this table to show the order of the events in the extract.

Event	Order in extract
Looks for tickets	
Puts milk bottles outside	
Wakes up	1
Has an accident in the kitchen	
Puts front door keys with tickets	

Q2 Write out the part of the text that gives you a clue about what kind of tickets Mrs Hanrahan is searching for.

Q3 Write out the part of the text that tells you about the accident in the first paragraph.

Q4 Copy out the answer that best describes the accident.

i) Mrs Hanrahan ate some Chinese takeaway, and then dropped a plate.

ii) Mrs Hanrahan knocked over two dirty dishes, and they smashed on the floor.

iii) Mrs Hanrahan knocked over two dirty dishes, and they landed in the bin.

Q5 What happens as Mrs Hanrahan is putting the milk bottles outside?

Q6 Write a paragraph explaining what you think might happen next in the story.

Artists against rabbits

Point, Example, Explanation

P.E.E.ing is a great way to write an answer. It stands for: make a POINT, give an EXAMPLE from the text, then give an EXPLANATION of what it means.

Questions 1-3 are about the following short extract.

> "I think we should get rid of the whole stinking lot," said Hanif, pointing at the rabbits.

Q1   Write a sentence commenting on how Hanif feels about the rabbits.

Q2   Which of the following sentences uses evidence from the extract to show how Hanif feels about the rabbits?

  i)   Hanif wants to get rid of the rabbits.

  ii)   Hanif wants to get rid of the rabbits. He shouts, which shows he doesn't like them.

  iii) Hanif wants to get rid of the rabbits. He calls them "stinking", which shows that he doesn't like them.

Q3   What does this tell the reader about Hanif? Copy out the correct answer.

  i)   Hanif has a strong opinion about the rabbits.

  ii)   Hanif is depressed, and hates everything in the world.

  iii) Hanif is a bully who goes around annoying other people.

Questions 4-6 are about the extract below.

> Milla glanced around the street nervously before she dumped the envelope in the bin.

Q4   What is Milla's mood in this extract?

Q5   Write out the part of the text that backs up your answer to **Q4**.

Q6   What does this tell the reader about Milla? Copy out the correct answer.

  i)   Milla doesn't like using bins in the street.

  ii)   Milla seems to be worried that someone will see her dumping the envelope in the bin.

  iii) Milla doesn't care what anyone thinks about her dumping the envelope in the bin.

Question 7 is about the extract below.

> "I'll be fine — don't worry about me," said Miles, with the hint of a tear in his eye.

Q7   How is Miles feeling in this extract? Give evidence from the text in your answer.

Different Types of Text

As soon as you start reading a text you should be thinking about what <u>type</u> of text it is. Work out whether it's fiction (made up) or non-fiction (fact). Here's some handy practice.

A

Five per cent of the population will suffer from an epileptic seizure at some time in their life, writes health expert Gareth Johns. Epilepsy affects 450,000 people in the UK, usually under-20-year-olds and those over 60. Seizures involve loss of consciousness and may affect memory or mood.

B

Watching the tutting clock,
Only six more minutes until I can be *there* and not *here*.
Gazing out through dusty panes,
Following the inkblot shadows of clouds with my eyes.
Outside, sunlight plays on the ground like an excitable child,
And a bird shouts with happiness.

C

Toby proceeded to mow the lawn like a man resigned to a long stretch in prison.

Being a very gentle soul, his only reaction when his wife bellowed that he had mown over her rose garden was to gently let the engine sputter to a forlorn halt. All that remained was a glacial silence, and a partially cut lawn.

D

In order to get the best results from your new T-300 kitchen juicer, please note the following points:
1) Always make a clear space around the T-300 in case of spray.
2) Avoid juicing soft fruits such as bananas. The residue will be difficult to clear from the workings of the T-300 after use.

Q1 Copy out each title below and write down which text each one goes with — A, B, C or D.

<u>Epilepsy — The Facts</u>   <u>Using your T-300</u>   <u>Waiting</u>   <u>A Man Alone</u>

Q2 Which texts are examples of non-fiction?

Q3 Write out each of the labels below and decide whether they apply to A, B, C or D.

Poem   Story   Manual   Magazine article

Q4 Decide whether the following bits of information are facts or opinions.

a) Epilepsy affects 450,000 people in the UK.

b) Birds are always really happy.

c) It wasn't Toby's fault that he ruined his wife's rose garden.

d) Soft fruit residue will be difficult to clear from the T-300 after use.

Oh, it's good to be alive.

Choice of Vocabulary

Writers choose their vocabulary (their words) carefully. Answer these questions to see if you know when and why writers use certain types of vocabulary in their texts.

Q1 Match up the type of vocabulary you would use with each type of text.

Type of Vocabulary	Type of Text
technical language	a story for a young child
formal language	a science textbook
simple language	a letter from the council

Q2 Why do you think the writer of 'Celeb-Watch!' chose to use slang in the text below?

CELEB-WATCH!

In this week's 'Celeb-Watch!', we found out all about Hollywood hunk Hank Harris's new squeeze. She's a real stunner! The happy couple seemed totally loved-up when we snapped them on the beach together in Honolulu.

Q3 Why do you think Charles Dickens chose to use slang in the extract below?

An extract from *Oliver Twist* by Charles Dickens

"Do you live in London?" inquired Oliver.

"Yes. I do, when I'm at home," replied the boy. "I suppose you want some place to sleep in to-night, don't you?'

"I do, indeed," answered Oliver. "I have not slept under a roof since I left the country."

"Don't fret your eyelids on that score," said the young gentleman. "I've got to be in London to-night; and I know a 'spectable old gentleman as lives there, wot'll give you lodgings for nothink, and never ask for the change—that is, if any genelman he knows interduces you..."

Q4 Which of the following statements about technical language is true? Write out the correct statement.

i) Writers use technical language to make a topic easier to understand.

ii) Technical language shows that a writer knows a lot about a subject.

iii) Writers only use technical language to show off.

Similes and Metaphors

Writers often use similes and metaphors in their descriptive writing.
Use the questions on this page to make sure you can tell the difference between them.

> A gig review from a music newspaper
>
> Any really great rock band knows that you have to keep your audience waiting. By the time The Brums arrived on stage, the audience were howling like wolves. Right from the start, singer Leo Ryder was a monster, roaring into the microphone. Guitarist Arnie X was possessed by the ghost of Jimi Hendrix as he played the most frantic guitar solos this side of Wigan. Jay Bryson beat the drums as if they were fires to be put out, but somehow managed to keep time as faithfully as an honest referee.
>
> As soon as the band launched into their number 2 hit, 'The First Rule is...', the audience were like a seething wave of noise. If it wasn't already clear, this concert proves that The Brums are rock music heavyweights — and they certainly don't pull any punches.

Q1 Write 'metaphor', 'simile' or 'neither' next to each of these phrases.

a) you have to keep your audience waiting

b) the audience were like a seething wave of noise

c) The Brums are rock music heavyweights

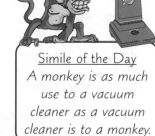

> Simile of the Day
> A monkey is as much use to a vacuum cleaner as a vacuum cleaner is to a monkey.

Q2 Which of these answers best explains why the writer describes the audience as "howling like wolves"?

i) The shouting audience sounded quiet and tuneful, like wolf howls.

ii) The shouting audience sounded noisy and tuneless, like wolf howls.

iii) The audience were eating raw meat and were very hairy.

Q3 Is the description in **Q2** a simile or a metaphor?

Q4 Copy and complete the table showing the similes and metaphors that the writer uses.

Thing being described	Description the writer uses	Simile or Metaphor	What this means
Leo Ryder			
Arnie X playing guitar			
Jay Bryson beating the drums			

Hello, I'm three — I've never metaphor before...

Fictional writing uses shiploads of metaphors and similes. They're imported from Greece, although some arrive on the black market to avoid customs tax. Learn to spot 'em. Without binoculars.

Personification, Alliteration and Onomatopoeia

Personification, alliteration and onomatopoeia all make a text more interesting to read.

Q1   Match up the boxes to complete the examples of personification.

The willow tree		wailed noisily.
The chest		waved its boughs frantically.
The moon		waited patiently to be opened.
The wind		hid shyly behind the clouds.

Q2   Write a description of each thing below, using alliteration to make it more effective.

e.g. snake *The snake slithered subtly across the sparkling sand.*

a) storm

b) cat

Q3   Write a list of onomatopoeic words that you could use to describe each thing.

e.g. piano music *crash, plink-plonk, trill, murmur...*

a) an explosion

b) a motorcycle race

Q4   Write out an example of each of the following things from the newspaper article below.

a) alliteration

b) onomatopoeia

c) personification

Terrifying Twister Terrorises Town

The quiet town of Marleysham was hit by a freak tornado yesterday. Although no one was injured, the residents are still in shock.

Mr Geale, who witnessed the tornado, said, "At first I heard this distant whooshing noise, but it got louder and louder. It sounded like a train passing right down the street. That's when I went to the window and saw it. I could hardly believe my eyes."

Local storm enthusiast Tilly McDuffel said, "I got in my car and drove after it, trying to get some footage. At one point I got right up close. As I was filming, I felt that it was staring right back at me. It was amazing."

Imagery

Imagery is about creating a picture in the reader's mind. Writers do this using descriptions. Think about the image the writer is trying to create, and what effect this has on the reader.

An extract from the novella *The Case of the Missing Relic*

Tonight, the whole city seemed silent. Even the birds were asleep, and not a sound disturbed the eerie quiet. The river flowed gently past the houses as if it didn't want to wake up the slumbering inhabitants.

Inspector Graham paced the damp, dark streets, expecting trouble at any moment. He gazed up at the pale moon which lit the streets below, and held his gas lamp out with a trembling hand. He soon reached his destination. His heart hammered like a drum in his chest. In front of him he could make out the grey archway of a narrow doorway. The night before he had come across a pack of snarling dogs guarding it, but tonight they were absent. The door opened with a low creak at his push and he stepped cautiously over the threshold.

The room was an icy tomb, and his breath came out in clouds in front of him. He raised his lamp to cast a flickering glow over the dim inside of the room. The only furniture was a broad farmhouse table, upon which were several items — a cotton glove, a faded yellow sheet of paper, and a small stone carving of a man crouching as if about to pounce at the Inspector.

Q1 Write out an example of a simile from the text, and explain why you think the writer has chosen to use it.

Q2 a) In the last paragraph, the writer uses a metaphor to describe the room Inspector Graham walks into. Write it out.

b) What effect does this metaphor have on the reader?

Q3 Write out the part of the text that describes the stone carving.

Q4 Write out the statement that explains the effect of the description in **Q3**.

i) The stone carving is described as if it is alive — this effect is called alliteration.

ii) The stone carving is described as if it is alive — this effect is called onomatopoeia.

iii) The stone carving is described as if it is alive — this effect is called personification.

Q5 Write out another part of the text that uses the same effect.

Mood

Fiction writers build up the mood of a scene through the language they use. Mood is about how the text <u>makes you feel</u> — whether it's happy, sad, funny, frightening, exciting...

A At last the waiting was over. Rachel held the exam results envelope and watched her friends opening theirs. Some smiled with relief, some stared at the floor.

Her fingers tugged gently at the envelope.

Slightly open now...

Nearly there...

B The mood took hold of the family like a virus. Mealtimes were now a matter of muttered greetings, lowered eyes and shared silences. Even the cracked ceilings had begun to weep rainwater. Gordon knew that Dexter had been *only* a dog, but he was missed like a member of the family.

C Katie strolled amid the laughing guests, her son Daniel trotting at her side. The sun caressed Katie's skin, while a cool breeze tickled the hair falling on her neck. The grass beneath her feet provided a soft carpet. Katie hadn't felt so alive in years.

Q1 Match up each of the texts A, B and C to one of the moods below.

tense   romantic   happy   horrific   funny   sad

Q2 In text A, is Rachel in a hurry to open the envelope?
Use evidence from the extract to back up your answer.

Q3 Why do you think the writer of text B used the word "weep" instead of "let in"? Mention the overall mood of the text in your answer.

Q4 What does the word "trotting" in text C tell you about how Daniel feels?

Q5 What effect do the short sentences at the end of text A have? Write out the correct answer.

i) They slow the pace down before Rachel opens the envelope, which builds up suspense.

ii) They speed the pace up before Rachel opens the envelope, which creates a sense of excitement.

Q6 Which of the three texts would the sentence below fit into?
Write a sentence to explain your answer.

Sadness hung heavily in the still air of the house.

Q7 Write a couple of sentences explaining what the phrase "muttered greetings, lowered eyes and shared silences" from text B tells you about the mood of the text.

Layout

Some texts are laid out in a special way, e.g. with bullet points, headings or arrows.
Look at the following three extracts and answer the questions below.

A
Tues 3rd Feb — Video camera finally arrived! Can't believe it took three weeks to get here.

Wed 4th Feb — Been playing with camera all day. Caroline came round, and we wrote and filmed a pretend TV show. I got to be the game show host (naturally).

Thu 5th Feb — Dropped camera when I was trying to film myself on a skateboard — it doesn't look too healthy anymore. Think I might take up photography instead.

B
<u>Why go to the Lake District?</u> It may not be the most 'happening' place, but there are often locally produced performances in Kendal, or specialist art films showing at the cinema.

<u>What's in the local area?</u> Well, most people go to the Lake District to walk in the hills. If you're less of an outdoor type, there are plenty of other diversions. The 'Theatre by the Lake' in Keswick is well worth a look.

<u>Does anyone care about the Lake District?</u> The Royal Shakespeare Company regularly tour Keswick and Kendal. The arts centre in Kendal is a member of the British Film Institute, so it often shows restored classic films.

C
Five tips for a healthy computer:
1. Always shut down the computer correctly after use.
2. Try not to have more than three applications running at once.
3. Regularly scan your computer for viruses.
4. Make sure your computer base unit is well ventilated.
5. Don't eat or drink near your computer.

> Using lots of programs at once will slow your computer down.

> See next page for more on viruses.

> Don't block the fan at the back of the unit, or it will overheat.

Q1 What kind of text do you think Extract A is taken from? Explain your answer.

Q2 Explain why it's important that the writer of Extract A included dates as subheadings.

Q3 Why are the subheadings in Extract B written as questions? Write out the best answer.

  i) To make the article feel like a speech read out by the writer.

  ii) To make the article feel like a conversation between the writer and the reader.

  iii) To annoy the reader and to make them feel stupid.

Q4 Why has the writer of Extract C numbered the five points?

Q5 Explain the purpose of the information in grey boxes in Extract C.

Q6 How do the arrows in Extract C help the reader to understand the text?

Structure

As well as layout, writers have to think about the order they put their information in. You may come across questions about structure, e.g. what makes a good introduction or conclusion...

A book review for a popular magazine

> If asked about writer Andrew Bright, most people would react: "Who?" However, all this is about to change...
>
> Bright's new novel, 'A Tale of Two Celebrities', is a vicious attack on the nature of celebrity in the 21st century. Set in present-day Manchester, it tells the story of the rivalry between failing TV host Richard and rising star Penelope.
>
> The novel's fans (and there will be many) will applaud the author's bold statements and the unflinching satire of our obsession with celebrities. The book is sure to do brisk business, and is likely to be a big-seller in airports and newsagents.
>
> On the other hand, many people will scoff at the two-dimensional characters, as well as the unsatisfying ending (in which Richard and Penelope fight it out on air in a duel-like ratings war).
>
> So, next time someone asks you about Andrew Bright, you'd better have read 'A Tale of Two Celebrities', so that you know where you stand.

Q1 Explain one way in which the first paragraph is effective as an introduction to the article.

Q2 Write a sentence to sum up what the writer tells you in the second paragraph.

Q3 Why do you think the writer put that paragraph straight after the introduction?

Q4 Sum up the differences between paragraphs 3 and 4, in one sentence.

Q5 Why do you think the writer put paragraphs 3 and 4 next to each other?

Q6 Write out the answer below that explains why the last sentence is a good ending to the text.

  i) The last sentence refers back to the introduction and sums up the main point of the review.

  ii) The last sentence makes a new point that is better than the other points in the text.

  iii) The last sentence tries to persuade the reader that 'A Tale of Two Celebrities' is terrible.

Q7 Explain how the writer structures the book review in a way that keeps the reader interested. Write about half a page and use your answers to the above questions to help you.

Structure — point don't I it of see the...

Writing needs to be well structured in order to get information across to the reader in a clear and logical way. Some might say it's as important as regular teeth-brushing — so best pay attention.

Stories

There are lots of features used in stories that you have to know about: perspective, plot, themes, characterisation... Have a go at these questions to see if you're getting to grips with them.

Q1   Write down whether these sentences are written in the first person or the third person.

a)   Isabel ploughed on through the wind and snow. She needed to get to the cabin.

b)   I gripped onto the safety bars of the roller coaster until my knuckles were white.

c)   We ran away laughing — our booby trap had worked.

d)   They lay back on the sand, enjoying the sun on their faces. School was finally over.

Q2   A story's plot has been jumbled up below. Write out the plot points in the correct order.

i)   Huddled up in the tree, they hear scary noises in the woods.

iv)   They decide to take shelter for the night in a hollow tree.

ii)   Sam and Kelly go for a walk in the woods.

v)   They get lost and night begins to fall.

iii)   The rescue party take them safely home and they fall asleep on the sofa.

vi)   They realise that the noise is a rescue party that has come looking for them.

The story of Mulan

In China, many hundreds of years ago, there lived a young girl called Mulan. Mulan lived with her father, who had once been a famous warrior. Although he was now old and unwell, he had taught Mulan how to fight and use a sword.

One day, a messenger came to Mulan's village. He announced that China was at war. By order of the Emperor, every family had to send one man to fight.

Mulan clenched her fists. Her father was so frail that surely he would not survive long in a war. She knew what she had to do.

That night, she crept into her father's room. He was sleeping deeply so she had no trouble taking the things she needed: some men's clothes and her father's old sword. She saddled her father's horse and before long she was ready to leave. She gritted her teeth and, without looking back over her shoulder, she rode off to join the army.

Q3   What do you think is the main theme of this story? Explain your answer.

magic   bravery   romance   good against evil   loneliness

Q4   In the text, Mulan "gritted her teeth". What does this show? Write out the best answer.

i)   It shows that she is angry with the Chinese Emperor.

ii)   It shows that she is determined to join the army in place of her father.

iii)   It shows that she is jealous that her father will not have to fight.

Poetry

Poets have to choose their words carefully, just like other writers.
They also need to think about the structure, rhythm and rhyme of their poems.

Q1 Copy out the following verses, and choose a line from the box to complete each one.

a) The Owl and the Pussy-Cat went to sea
In a beautiful pea-green boat.
They took some honey, and plenty of money,
....

(Edward Lear)

b) Two households, both alike in dignity
In fair Verona, where we lay our scene
From ancient grudge break to new mutiny
....

c) There was an old man from Crewe
Who found he had nothing to do
So he sat on the stairs,
And counted his hairs
....

d) Tyger! Tyger! Burning bright,
....
What immortal hand or eye,
Could frame thy fearful symmetry?

(William Blake)

e) Round, golden and warm
Gives life to all who dwell there
....

Where civil blood makes civil hands unclean.
In the forests of the night,
Wrapped up in a five-pound note.
Glorious, the sun.
And found that he only had two.

Q2 The above verses are examples of different forms of poetry.
Copy out the definitions below and match them to the correct example from **Q1**.

a) A <u>limerick</u> has five lines. The first two rhyme together, the third and fourth lines rhyme with each other, and the fifth line rhymes with the first two.

b) A <u>sonnet</u> is a fourteen-line poem with ten syllables in each line. There are different rhyme patterns for different types of sonnet.

c) A <u>haiku</u> is a three-line Japanese poem. The first and last lines have five syllables each, and the middle line has seven syllables.

d) An example of a <u>regular rhyming pattern</u> is when every other line rhymes. This pattern goes all the way through the poem.

e) Another example of a regular rhyming pattern is <u>rhyming couplets</u>. This is when pairs of lines rhyme together.

Q3 Copy and complete the paragraph below, using the words from the box.

A verse is the same thing as a .... Each verse is made up of a group of .... Verses in a poem have .... words but they often follow the .... pattern of syllables and ....

same	rhyming	stanza	lines	different

Comparing Texts

Reading questions often ask you to compare different texts. Read through these texts, then turn the page and have a go at answering the questions. Yeah, loads of fun, I know...

A scientific account called *The Macaque Monkeys of Japan*

Day 1 — Macaque monkeys currently living in the centre of the island, within the forest area. Monkeys' day-to-day activities seem to be entirely according to accepted theories. Diet seems to be largely composed of berries.

Day 2 — Team placed large amount of potatoes in forest. May have to wait a while to see if the macaques show any interest.

Day 6 — It worked! Two days ago, the monkeys showed some interest in the potatoes — since then they have made potatoes the main part of their diet. Team intends to move piles of potatoes closer to shore to see if the macaques follow.

Day 9 — Macaques definitely becoming comfortable with living on shoreline now, entirely dependant on potatoes we supply. I even saw one monkey washing a potato in the sea before eating it! This development is entirely unprecedented — seems to prove that monkeys are capable of dramatically changing their living patterns.

Day 11 — Macaques now entirely at home by shoreline. A few making efforts to learn to swim in sea, and others starting to copy. Experiment declared a success — the macaques are learning afresh how to live their day-to-day life.

> Monkeys of the World Unite!
> You have Nothing to Lose but your Bananas

An extract from the novel *I, Monkey*

This is getting ridiculous. It was just a bit of fun letting the humans teach me sign language (and it really wasn't hard to learn) — but now they're excited and buzzing around like annoying flies. They've started saying that I'm the first ape to show real intelligence — the cheek of it! Just because we don't usually choose to humour their dreary experiments doesn't mean that we aren't capable of getting a message across.

Lots of people have come to visit since I started answering back through sign language. Most of them are pretty sad specimens with faces as pale as their white coats. I was going to give them a nice surprise by saying a few words, maybe have a chat about the weather — but it's getting boring now, so I think I might just be on my way.

An extract from an article called *Monkey Behaviour*

instinct = in-built patterns of behaviour in response to certain things

Humans may learn a lot from insects and animals. Humans will always question what they're doing and why they're doing it — but, for instance, a worker bee will always know its role in the beehive. It may feed the young or guard the hive, but it will always carry out its duty without even needing to be told. The same is true of more 'intelligent' organisms, such as the monkey. Although monkeys can be taught tricks, they are not able to break out of the simple instinctive pattern which instructs them exactly how to live their lives.

> Too right. Down with this sort of thing.

Comparing Texts

Keep turning the page to check the texts while you're doing these questions.

Q1   Match up each text to its description.

The Macaque Monkeys of Japan	Story
I, Monkey	Magazine article
Monkey Behaviour	Diary

Q2   Write out a phrase from *I, Monkey* that contains a simile.

Q3   Write out a phrase from *I, Monkey* that uses humour.

Q4   Write out a sentence from *The Macaque Monkeys of Japan* that is written in informal language.

Q5   Why do you think the writer of *The Macaque Monkeys of Japan* decided to break up the text into sections?

Q6   Which of these phrases from *The Macaque Monkeys of Japan* gives a fact rather than an opinion?

i)   Macaque monkeys currently living in the centre of the island

ii) seems to prove that monkeys are capable of dramatically changing their living patterns

iii) the macaques are learning afresh how to live their day-to-day life

Q7   Write out the paragraph that sums up what happens in the extract from *I, Monkey*.

i)   The scientists believe that monkeys are only capable of learning very basic sign language. The scientists are clever, so they are probably right.

ii) The monkey is more intelligent than the scientists realise. The monkey tells the story from his point of view, which shows the scientists are wrong.

Q8   Write out the paragraph that sums up the writer's opinion in *Monkey Behaviour*.

i)   The writer thinks that humans are not ruled by instinct, but that all animals and insects are.

ii) The writer thinks that humans are ruled by instinct, but animals and insects are not.

iii) The writer thinks that all animals, including humans, are completely ruled by instinct.

Comparing Texts

Now you can move on to longer comparing questions. When comparing two texts, make sure you don't write too much on one — write an equal amount on each. Nice and balanced.

Q9 Write out the sentence that best describes the main idea in all three texts.

i) All three texts are about whether monkeys can instinctively talk.

ii) All three texts are about whether the behaviour of monkeys is purely instinctive.

iii) All three texts are about whether monkeys know that their behaviour is instinctive.

Q10 Copy and complete this table comparing all three texts.
Use your answers to the questions on the previous page to help you.

Name of extract	The Macaque Monkeys of Japan	I, Monkey	Monkey Behaviour
Is the extract fiction or non-fiction?			
Is the language formal or informal?			
Is there a first-person narrator?			
Does the writer use facts to back up their points?			
Does the writer think that animals are ruled by instinct?			

Now make use of your answers so far to answer the next three questions.
The table above is going to be especially useful.

Q11 Re-read *The Macaque Monkeys of Japan* and *I, Monkey*. Write a short description of the differences between the layout of each of the texts.

Q12 Re-read *I, Monkey* and *Monkey Behaviour*. Write a paragraph describing the differences between the language used in each of the texts.

Q13 Re-read *The Macaque Monkeys of Japan* and *Monkey Behaviour*. Write a paragraph describing the differences between the writers' opinions about animal instinct.

"Romeo and Julie — do I get my banana now?" (monkey 5882)
Don't forget to write the same amount on each of the texts you are comparing — otherwise one of them is bound to feel left out and get upset — and who needs a whimpering text on their hands?

Practice Questions

Time to try your hand at dealing with some longer texts — no need to panic, just consider it a sort of challenge. Read the extract below, and have a go at the questions opposite.

This is an extract from the short story *The Sea Raiders* by H G Wells.

Mr Fison, torn by curiosity, began picking his way across the wave-worn rocks, and, finding the wet seaweed that covered them thickly **rendered** them extremely slippery, he stopped, removed his shoes and socks, and coiled his trousers above his knees. His object was, of course, merely to avoid stumbling into the rocky pools about him, and perhaps he was rather glad, as all men are, of an excuse to resume, even for a moment, the sensations of his boyhood. At any rate, it is to this, no doubt, that he owes his life.

He approached his mark with all the assurance which the absolute security of this country against all forms of animal life gives its inhabitants. The round bodies moved to and fro, but it was only when he surmounted the **skerry** of boulders I have mentioned that he realised the horrible nature of the discovery. It came upon him with some suddenness.

The rounded bodies fell apart as he came into sight over the ridge, and displayed the pinkish object to be the partially devoured body of a human being, but whether of a man or woman he was unable to say. And the rounded bodies were new and ghastly looking creatures, in shape somewhat resembling an octopus, and with huge and very long and flexible tentacles, coiled copiously on the ground. The skin had a glistening texture, unpleasant to see, like shiny leather. The downward bend of the tentacle-surrounded mouth, the curious **excrescence** at the bend, the tentacles, and the large intelligent eyes, gave the creatures a grotesque suggestion of a face. They were the size of a fair-sized swine about the body, and the tentacles seemed to him to be many feet in length. There were, he thinks, seven or eight at least of the creatures. Twenty yards beyond them, amid the surf of the now returning tide, two others were emerging from the sea.

Their bodies lay flatly on the rocks, and their eyes regarded him with evil interest; but it does not appear that Mr Fison was afraid, or that he realised that he was in any danger. Possibly his confidence is to be ascribed to the limpness of their attitudes. But he was horrified, of course, and intensely excited and indignant at such revolting creatures preying upon human flesh. He thought they had chanced upon a drowned body. He shouted to them, with the idea of driving them off, and, finding they did not budge, cast about him, picked up a big rounded lump of rock, and flung it at one.

And then, slowly uncoiling their tentacles, they all began moving towards him — creeping at first deliberately, and making a soft purring sound to each other.

rendered = made
skerry = mound
excrescence = growth

Practice Questions

OK, so maybe 'The Sea Raiders' is gruesome and bloodthirsty, but it's also full of descriptions and other tricks that all good writers use. Answer these questions about it.

Q1 Read the third paragraph carefully and write out any phrases that describe what the creatures look like.

New and ghastly looking, in a shape resembling an octopus, huge and very long flexible tentacles, coiled copiously on the ground.

Q2 Quickly sketch a picture of one of the creatures, using descriptions from the third paragraph.

Q3 Which of the following extracts from the text contains a simile? Copy the correct answer.

  i) And the rounded bodies were new and ghastly looking creatures...

  ii) The skin had a glistening texture, unpleasant to see, like shiny leather.

  iii) Their bodies lay flatly on the rocks, and their eyes regarded him with evil interest;

  iv) They were the size of a fair-sized swine...

Q4 Write out any words from the fourth paragraph of the extract that tell you about Mr Fison's reaction to the creatures.

Their eyes regarded him with evil interest but it did not appear Mr Fison was afraid but he was horrified of course and intensely excited and indignant at such revolting creatures preying upon human flesh

Q5 Write out any parts of the text that give you the impression that the creatures are as intelligent as humans.

When Mr Fison shouted at them they didn't move, they just picked up a rock and threw it at Mr Fison. or made soft purring noises to each other

Q6 Write out any parts of the text that tell you about how the creatures move.

they slowly uncoiled their tentacles and began moving towards him

Q7 Which row of the table sums up how the creatures move and what effect the movement achieves?

	How the creatures move	Effect this achieves
i)	Very slowly	Makes the reader feel sad
ii)	Very quickly	Makes the text funnier
iii)	Very slowly	Builds up suspense
iv)	Very quickly	Builds up suspense

Q8 In the extract from *The Sea Raiders*, how does the writer convey the horror of the situation to the reader? Write half a page, using the questions on this page for help.

Life lesson — don't throw rocks at sea monsters...

Don't read the text just once — keep looking back at it when you're doing the questions.
Pick out the bit of the text that each question refers to, and then read that bit again carefully.

24

Practice Questions

Pages 25-26 are about breaking tricky questions down into manageable chunks. Read the extract below and then have a go at the questions, referring back whenever you need to.

This is an abridged extract from the novel *The Picture of Dorian Gray* by Oscar Wilde.

After about a quarter of an hour, Hallward stopped painting, looked for a long time at Dorian Gray, and then for a long time at the picture, biting the end of one of his huge brushes, and smiling. "It is quite finished," he cried, at last, and stooping down he wrote his name in thin vermilion letters on the left-hand corner of the canvas.

Lord Henry came over and examined the picture. It was certainly a wonderful work of art, and a wonderful likeness as well.

"My dear fellow, I congratulate you most warmly," he said. "Mr. Gray, come and look at yourself."

The lad started, as if awakened from some dream. "Is it really finished?" he murmured, stepping down from the platform.

"Quite finished," said Hallward. "And you have sat splendidly to-day. I am awfully obliged to you."

"That is entirely due to me," broke in Lord Henry. "Isn't it, Mr. Gray?"

Dorian made no answer, but passed listlessly in front of his picture and turned towards it. When he saw it he drew back, and his cheeks flushed for a moment with pleasure. A look of joy came into his eyes, as if he had recognized himself for the first time. He stood there motionless, and in wonder, dimly conscious that Hallward was speaking to him, but not catching the meaning of his words. The sense of his own beauty came on him like a revelation. He had never felt it before. Basil Hallward's compliments had seemed to him to be merely the charming exaggerations of friendship. He had listened to them, laughed at them, forgotten them. They had not influenced his nature. Then had come Lord Henry, with his strange **panegyric** on youth, his terrible warning of its brevity. That had stirred him at the time, and now, as he stood gazing at the shadow of his own loveliness, the full reality of the description flashed across him. Yes, there would be a day when his face would be wrinkled and wizen, his eyes dim and colourless, the grace of his figure broken and deformed. The scarlet would pass away from his lips, and the gold steal from his hair. The life that was to make his soul would mar his body. He would become ignoble, hideous, and uncouth.

As he thought of it, a sharp pang of pain struck like a knife across him, and made each delicate fibre of his nature quiver. His eyes deepened into amethyst, and a mist of tears came across them. He felt as if a hand of ice had been laid upon his heart.

"Don't you like it?" cried Hallward at last, stung a little by the lad's silence, and not understanding what it meant.

"Of course he likes it," said Lord Henry. "Who wouldn't like it? It is one of the greatest things in modern art. I will give you anything you like to ask for it. I must have it."

"It is not my property, Harry."

"Whose property is it?"

"Dorian's, of course."

"He is a very lucky fellow."

panegyric = a speech in praise of something

"How sad it is!" murmured Dorian Gray, with his eyes still fixed upon his own portrait. "How sad it is! I shall grow old, and horrid, and dreadful. But this picture will remain always young. It will never be older than this particular day of June. . . . If it was only the other way! If it was I who were to be always young, and the picture that were to grow old! For this—for this—I would give everything! Yes, there is nothing in the whole world I would not give!"

Practice Questions

You might get given a question with prompts, which are hints that help you answer the question.
If there are no prompts — make your own to remind you of what your answer needs to cover.

Q1 Copy out **two** phrases that suggest that Dorian is vulnerable and sensitive.

1) A mist of tears

2) made each delicate fibre of his nature quiver

Q2 Why does Hallward think that Dorian might not like the picture?

It's because Dorian doesn't say anything

Q3 Write out **one** phrase from the last paragraph which
shows that Dorian is desperate to stay young.

there is a thing in the whole world I would not give

Q4 Copy out and correct the answer to the question below.

> Explain how Oscar Wilde's use of similes and metaphors
> conveys Dorian's state of mind in the extract.

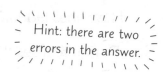

Hint: there are two
errors in the answer.

*Wilde writes that "a sharp pang of pain struck like a knife across him", and
this <u>metaphor</u> shows that Dorian feels physically hurt when he realises
that he will grow old. Then Dorian <u>calms down again</u> when Wilde writes
that "he felt as if a hand of ice had been laid upon his heart".*

simile, panics

Q5 Write out the box of three prompts that would help you to answer the question below.

> Comment on the way that Lord Henry and Basil Hallward act towards Dorian Gray.

> **How does Hallward react to Lord Henry?**
> **How does Lord Henry react to Hallward?**
> **How does Dorian feel about the painting?**

> **What does Hallward say to Dorian?**
> **How does Hallward feel about the painting?**
> **What does Lord Henry say to Dorian?**

Q6 Explain why the group of three prompts that you didn't pick in **Q5** would be unsuitable.

*The first two prompts ask how Lord Henry and Hallward act towards each
other not towards Dorian the third prompt doesn't have anything to do with
Lord Henry and Basil Hallward's actions to Dorian, it's just how Dorian sees about the painting.*

Q7 Write a list of **three** prompts that would help you answer the question below.

> What is Dorian Gray's opinion of old age by the end of the extract?

He thinks being old is horrid and dreadful

Practice Questions

You'll probably come across reading questions without prompts quite a bit, so some more practice would be really helpful... Oh, look — what a coincidence...

Q8   Write out the sentence that sums up Dorian's view of himself at the start of the extract.

ⓘ Dorian isn't really aware of his beauty and doesn't believe the compliments he gets.

ii) Dorian knows he is beautiful and loves hearing people say nice things about him.

iii) Dorian is vain and wants everyone to see his beautiful portrait. ✓

Q9   Copy out phrases from the text that back up your answer to **Q8**.
The sense of his own beauty came as a revelation to him. Basil's flattering compliments had seemed to him to be merely the charming exaggerations of friendship ✓

Q10   What happens in the text to make Dorian change his opinion of himself?
He sees the painting of himself ✓

Q11   How does Dorian feel about his appearance afterwards? Write out the correct answer.

i)   Dorian realises that he is not as beautiful as he thought beforehand.

ⓘⓘ Dorian realises that he is as beautiful as people have been telling him.

iii) Dorian wishes that he was even more beautiful than he already is. ✓

...because I'm worth it.

Q12   Copy out a phrase from the text that backs up your answer to **Q11**.
The sense of his beauty came on him as a revelation ✓

Q13   How does Dorian feel about growing old? Copy and correct this answer.

Dorian imagines when his face will be "wrinkled and wizen" and he feels so horrified that the thought hurts "like a <u>sword</u> across him". He imagines when "the scarlet would pass away from his lips", which shows that he thinks that he will become ~~mean~~ as well as ugly.

Knife ✓

Hint: there are two errors in the answer.

Q14   What does Dorian wish for at the end of the extract?
What does this tell you about his feelings?
He wishes that he could stay young. This tells me he cares about ✓
how he looks.

Q15   Use **questions 8-14** to write a list of prompts to answer this question.

| How does Dorian Gray's opinion of himself change during the extract? |

Q16   Now answer the question above — (it's no biggy, honest). Your prompts and answers from the other questions on this page should help a lot.

Practice Questions

You know the drill — read the text carefully, have a go at the questions and refer back to this text whenever you need to. There are more questions this time — I'm confident you'll do fine.

An extract from a magazine article called *World Cup Fever*

A shrill blast. The 'thunk' of leather against leather. The air is filled with the sounds of shouting and stamping feet. Thousands of people with painted faces are snarling like hyenas at their opponents. No, this is not a scene from the film *Braveheart*. It's even more serious — it's the World Cup.

The World Cup was thought up by Jules Rimet in Paris, and the first Final was in 1930. The host, Uruguay, offered to pay for the travel expenses for the other teams. They were rewarded by winning, and declared a national day of holiday. Mind you, there were only 13 teams playing!

Where did football come from?

The history of football goes back ever so slightly further than 1930. The first records of the game were about 5000 years ago in China. Versions of football were also played by the ancient Greeks, Egyptians, and Romans. In the 16th century in Italy, a similar game called *calcio* was played, with a decapitated head used for the ball! In Britain we weren't much more humane either. Imagine the scene in medieval England: it's a national holiday and virtually every town in the country is turned into a bloody, sweaty battlefield that only faintly resembles a football pitch.

Later on, the British claimed the game as their own, before introducing it to countries around the world. In 1894 Charles Miller changed the face of Brazil for good when he left his boat carrying a football in each hand. Now many people recognise Brazil as the home of the most beautifully played football in the world.

The modern rules of football were only made concrete in 1863 when the Football Association was founded – and the game has slowly evolved into the one we know and love today.

Is it *really* the beautiful game?

So, the modern game of football has inspired and entertained people for decades, but it hasn't all been good. We're all aware of the phenomenon of football hooliganism. Although more and more regulations are being brought in to prevent disruption at matches, these idiots continue to spoil the game for many other people. However, football has been indirectly responsible for even worse things. In 1969 a controversial World Cup qualifying match between El Salvador and Honduras contributed to war breaking out between the two countries.

Practice Questions

What's so great about football?

Football is amazingly popular around the world. The largest stadium audience for a game was in Rio de Janeiro for the 1950 World Cup Final, when 200,000 people turned up to see the game. Nowadays, matches are transmitted live to the whole world on TV. In total, 3.2 billion people in 7 continents tuned into the 2010 World Cup — and there's only 6 billion people in the world, so that proves that the World Cup is pretty popular!

There are many ideas about why football is so popular around the world:

1. The basic rules are very simple – they don't need much explanation and so people can play football without even being able to talk the same language.

2. It doesn't take much organisation – all you need is a ball, a flat space of land and some markers for goalposts.

3. There's the potential for real drama – the game is very physical, and footballers can show off their skills.

Who are the biggest football fans?

During World Cup season in Brazil, walls and lampposts are often painted in the national team colours of green and yellow. In Britain we might not be quite as dramatic, but in 2010 we once again proved our devotion to football when thousands of people made excuses to miss school or work in order to watch the World Cup games held in South Africa.

Even those of us who wouldn't normally watch football managed to get caught up in the national excitement, including me...

...but I still don't understand the offside rule.

Practice Questions

Now it's high time that you put all your skills together to tackle some... um... more questions.
When you've read the article on p.27-28 have a go at these short questions.

Q1   Which country hosted the first World Cup?

Uraguay

Q2   Copy and complete the table below showing facts from the extract.

Description of fact	Number
Year of first World Cup Final	1930
Largest stadium audience	200,000
Year Football Association was created	1863
Total viewing figures of 2010 World Cup	3.2 billion
Year Charles Miller took football to Brazil	1894
Number of teams that played in first World Cup	13
Year World Cup match helped to start a war	1969

Q3   Write down the first country to play football on record, and how long ago that was.

China, 5000 years ago

Q4   Write down the two countries involved in a war following a World Cup match.

El Salvador and Honduras

Q5   Who originally thought up the idea of the World Cup?

Jules Rimet

Q6   Where was the World Cup created?

Paris

Q7   Why do you think the writer says that the "history of football goes back ever so slightly further than 1930"?

It's a joke

Q8   Why do you think the writer used the phrase "snarling like hyenas" to describe the football fans in the first paragraph?

It's a simile and he wants to write it so that the fans seem excited.

Q9   Why do you think the writer uses the phrase "bloody, sweaty battlefield" at the end of the third paragraph?

The phrase makes football game sound like battles

Q10   Explain why the writer numbered the points in the section "What's so great about football?".

To show that there are three separate ideas

Q11   Why do you think the writer uses questions for the subheadings?

To make the reader intrigued

Practice Questions

Thinking that the last page was a bit of a doddle? Well, this one's full of longer questions I'm afraid. Remember that it's often useful to break long questions down into smaller chunks.

Q12 Explain **one** way in which the first paragraph is effective as an introduction to the article. Use phrases from the text to back up your answer.

It is useful as it describes the atmosphere around the world cup. Showing like hyenas. Think of leader against leather

Q13 Copy and complete the table, by summing up each subsection in one sentence.

Subsection	Summary
Introduction	*Introducing world cup*
'Where did football come from?'	*origin of football*
'Is it really the beautiful game?'	*negative things on football*
'What's so great about football?'	*Why football is popular*
'Who are the biggest football fans?'	*fans at 2010 world cup*

Q14 Sum up the whole article in no more than **three** sentences.

The article explains the history of football and the world cup. It explains why football is popular

Q15 The section "Is it *really* the beautiful game?" is more negative than the rest of the text. Write out **one** phrase from this section that tells you the writer's opinion.

It hasn't all been good

Q16 Explain what Charles Miller did that "changed the face of Brazil".

He brought two footballs to Brazil.

Q17 Using facts from the text, write about **two** examples of football's violent history.

A war spoil the game so people, was broke out between two countries because of it.

Q18 Using facts from the text, give **three** reasons why football is extremely popular.

Simple game, very fun, doesn't take much organisation

Q19 Do you think the final sentence is a good ending to the text? Back up your answer with phrases from the text.

yes because it shows that football is a good and complicated game.

Q20 Sum up the writer's opinion of football, using evidence from the whole text to back up your answer.

He likes football

Q21 How does the writer use humour to keep the reader interested? Use phrases from the text to back up your answer.

Q22 In the whole article, explain how the writer presents the history of football as both positive and surprisingly violent.

Holy guacamole — it's the end of the reading section...

Blimey — that was a lot of questions to get through. Still, it's all fantastic practice. Then it'll all pay off when you stun your teachers with your incredible English skills. Honest.

Know Your Play

You <u>have</u> to know all about the story of the play you're studying, and a few basics on the characters. If you don't you'll be mighty stuck when it comes to writing an essay about 'em.

Q1   Write a short summary of each **act** in your play.

Q2   Write a few sentences to summarise each **scene** in the play you are studying.

Q3   Choose your favourite scene (one where lots of stuff happens).
Write a detailed summary of this scene.

Q4   Draw a storyboard for your chosen scene in **Q3**.

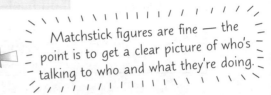
Matchstick figures are fine — the point is to get a clear picture of who's talking to who and what they're doing.

Q5   Sketch out a grid like this and fill it in for the main characters who appear in your play.

e.g.	Name	Job or title	Age	Appearance	Personality	Quotes
	Juliet	Daughter of Lord and Lady Capulet	13	Noble and rich Very beautiful	Lovely, but emotional	"my true love is grown to such excess..."

Q6   Using the examples below as guidelines, write a list of the main themes in the play you're studying. Find some quotes that are linked to each theme.

ROMEO AND JULIET
Forbidden love
Family
Honour
Death
Innocence

THE TEMPEST
Fate and justice
Magic
Freedom
Betrayal
Forgiveness

Don't go mad with your quotes — a couple to illustrate each theme will be fab.

Q7   Write down a one sentence definition for each of these words. If you don't know the answer look it up in a dictionary and rewrite the definition in your own words.

a) act

b) scene

c) character

d) tragedy

e) comedy

f) history play

g) prose

h) poetry

i) metre

j) exit

k) exeunt

l) aside

Summarising is easy — to cut a long story short...

Sometimes you'll have to write about specific parts of the play — maybe even specific scenes.
You might find it useful to make a summary of a play so that you know what's going on.

Understanding the Language

The hardest thing about Shakespeare is understanding the language. You can easily learn some of the common tricky words, but it's best if you try to <u>work out</u> what odd words mean.

Q1 The words on the left pop up all the time in Shakespeare. Write each of them out next to their modern meanings from the box on the right.

thy   ere   thou wilt

thee

hither   he hath   hie

thou art   thou hast

wherefore   hence   thou

from here   he has

your

before   you

you have

you are   you will

you   why   go   to here

Q2 Write down what you think each word in bold means.

a)

PARIS   I do defy thy **conjurations**,
           And apprehend thee for a **felon** here.
ROMEO   Wilt thou provoke me? Then have at thee, boy!
     ***Romeo and Juliet*, Act 5, Scene 3, lines 68-70**

Don't panic if you see a word you don't know — just <u>try</u> and work it out.

b)

PROSPERO   O Ferdinand!,
Do not smile at me that I boast her off,
For thou shalt find she will **outstrip** all praise,
And make it halt behind her.
     ***The Tempest*, Act 4, Scene 1, lines 8-11**

c)

CAPULET   Go to, go to,
You are a **saucy** boy. Is't so indeed?
This trick may chance to **scathe** you, I know what.
You must **contrary** me! Marry, 'tis time.
     ***Romeo and Juliet*, Act 1, Scene 5, lines 81-84**

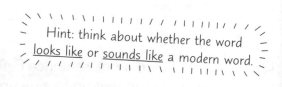

Hint: think about whether the word <u>looks like</u> or <u>sounds like</u> a modern word.

d)

SEBASTIAN   'Twas a sweet marriage, and we **prosper** well
             in our return.
ADRIAN   **Tunis** was never graced before with such a
          paragon to their queen.
     ***The Tempest*, Act 2, Scene 1, lines 71-74**

Understanding the Language

If you've got a rough idea what the characters are going on about, you're doing pretty well.
However, to test whether you really understand, try putting what they say into your own words.

Q3   Write this speech out in your own words.

> ALONSO   You cram these words into mine ears against
> The stomach of my sense. Would I had never
> Married my daughter there, for, coming thence,
> My son is lost, and, in my rate, she too,
> Who is so far from Italy removed
> I ne'er again shall see her. O thou mine heir
> Of Naples and of Milan, what strange fish
> Hath made his meal on thee?
>
> ***The Tempest*, Act 2, Scene 1, lines 104-111**

Q4   Write this speech out in simple, modern language.

> ROMEO   Thou cans't not speak of that thou dost not feel:
> Wert thou as young as I, Juliet thy love,
> An hour but married, Tybalt murderèd,
> Doting like me and like me banishèd,
> Then mightst thou speak, then mightst thou tear they hair,
> And fall upon the ground, as I do now,
> Taking the measure of an unmade grave.
>
> ***Romeo and Juliet*, Act 3, Scene 3, lines 64-70**

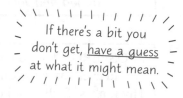

If there's a bit you
don't get, <u>have a guess</u>
at what it might mean.

Q5   You know what I'm going to say... Yep, write this speech out in your own words.

> PROSPERO   Behold, Sir King,
> The wronged Duke of Milan, Prospero.
> For more assurance that a living prince
> Does now speak to thee, I embrace they body,
> And to thee and thy company I bid
> A hearty welcome.
>
> ***The Tempest*, Act 5, Scene 1, lines 106-111**

A hearty welcome...

Q6   Choose an extract from your play that's at least
15 lines long. Write it out in your own words.

Art thou afeard o' the dreaded Shakespeare...

Well, ye need not be. The important thing is to give it a go. The more Shakespeare you read,
the easier it is to understand — which means all that 'thou hast, he hath' lark pays off in the end.

Backing Up Your Answers

You can have the world's brainiest ideas in your Shakespeare answers, but you'll get little recognition for your fine pieces of wisdom if you don't back them up with quotes.

Q1 Find the words in each extract which back up the statement on the right.

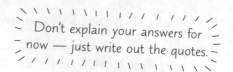
Don't explain your answers for now — just write out the quotes.

a)

> ROMEO   I do protest I never injured thee,
> But love thee better than thou canst devise,
> Till thou shalt know the reason of my love;
> And so, good Capulet, which name I tender
> As dearly as mine own, be satisfied.
> *Romeo and Juliet*, Act 3, Scene 1, lines 64-68

Romeo loves the Capulets as much as he loves his own family.

b)

> NURSE   But first let me tell ye, if ye should lead her into a fool's paradise, as they say, it were a very gross kind of behaviour, as they say: for the gentlewoman is young; and, therefore, if you should deal double with her, truly it were an ill thing to be offered to any gentlewoman, and very weak dealing.
> *Romeo and Juliet*, Act 2, Scene 4, lines 140-145

The Nurse warns Romeo that cheating on Juliet would be nasty.

c)

> PROSPERO   For you, most wicked sir, whom to call brother
> Would even infect my mouth, I do forgive
> Thy rankest fault — all of them — and require
> My dukedom of thee, which perforce I know
> Thou must restore.
> *The Tempest*, Act 5, Scene 1, lines 130-134

Prospero says he should sound angry with Antonio, even though he forgives him.

d)

> JULIET   Shall I speak ill of him that is my husband?
> Ah, poor my lord, what tongue shall smooth thy name,
> When I, thy three-hours wife, have mangled it?
> But wherefore, villain, didst thou kill my cousin?
> That villain cousin would have killed my husband.
> *Romeo and Juliet*, Act 3, Scene 2, lines 97-101

Juliet questions whether she should sound angry with Romeo.

e)

> PROSPERO   you demi-puppets that
> By moonshine do the green sour ringlets make,
> Whereof the ewe not bites; and you whose pastime
> Is to make midnight mushrooms, that rejoice
> To hear the solemn curfew; by whose aid —
> Weak masters though ye be — I have bedimmed
> The noontide sun, called forth the mutinous winds,
> And 'twixt the green sea and the azured vault
> Set roaring war.
> *The Tempest*, Act 5, Scene 1, lines 36-44

Prospero shows how powerful his magic is by using lots of natural imagery.

You can't just quote one bit for this one — you'll have to quote a few words.

Backing Up Your Answers

... more practice at finding words from the text to prove that your ideas are the product of full-blown genius. Remember to just write out the bit of the text that backs up the statement.

Q2   Find the words in each extract which back up the statement on the right.

a)

> FRIAR LAWRENCE   The sun not yet thy sighs from heaven clears,
> Thy old groans ring yet in my ancient ears.
> Lo, here upon thy cheek the stain doth sit
> Of an old tear that is not washed off yet.
>
> *Romeo and Juliet*, Act 2, Scene 3, lines 73-76

Friar Lawrence says it's not long since Romeo was crying about Rosaline.

b)

> CALIBAN   Why, as I told thee, 'tis a custom with him
> I' th' afternoon to sleep. There thou mayst brain him,
> Having first seized his books, or with a log
> Batter his skull, or paunch him with a stake,
> Or cut his wezand with thy knife. Remember
> First to possess his books
>
> *The Tempest*, Act 3, Scene 2, lines 87-92

Caliban wants Prospero's death to be painful and violent.

Find the different ways that Caliban suggests Stephano should kill Prospero.

c)

> MIRANDA   Sir, are not you my father?
> PROSPERO   Thy mother was a piece of virtue, and
> She said thou wast my daughter, and thy father
> Was Duke of Milan, and his only heir
> And princess, no worse issued.
> MIRANDA   O, the heavens!
> What foul play had we that came from thence?
> Or blessed was't we did?
>
> *The Tempest*, Act 1, Scene 2, lines 56-62

Miranda is surprised to find out that she is the daughter of the Duke of Milan.

You need to look for an expression of surprise...

d)

> ROMEO   I must indeed, and therefore came I hither.
> Good gentle youth, tempt not a desperate man.
> Fly hence, and leave me: think upon these gone.
> Let them affright thee. I beseech thee, youth,
> Put not another sin upon my head,
> By urging me to fury. O, be gone!
> By heaven, I love thee better than myself,
> For I come hither armed against myself.
> Stay not, be gone; live, and hereafter say,
> A madman's mercy bade thee run away.
>
> *Romeo and Juliet*, Act 5, Scene 3, lines 58-67

Romeo admits that he has done evil things in the past.

You can back this point up by saying that Romeo threatens Paris, showing he has an evil side.

Writing Your Answers

You make your point and you find a quote to back it up. Great. Then you've got to <u>explain</u> how the quote backs up your comment. It's not too hard — just don't forget to do it.

Here's something a bit easier to read as a break from all that Shakespeare...

> There once was a playwright called Kit
> Who wrote hit after hit after hit.
> Each day he used up forty goose-feather quills;
> Lords, ladies and gents all rated his skills —
> But the geese didn't like him one bit.

Q1   Work through these questions, then put your answers together to give a full answer to the question in the box.

   a)   Was Kit's work successful in the theatre, yes or no?

   b)   Which words tell you this?

   c)   Explain why these words show the work was successful.

According to the limerick, was Kit's work popular?

Q2   Work through these questions, then put your answers together to give a full answer to the question in the box.

   a)   Which words tell you that many people thought Kit was talented?

   b)   What techniques does the writer use? E.g. alliteration, repetition...

   c)   How do the effects that the writer uses add to the impression that people thought Kit was talented?

How does the writer emphasise Kit's popularity?

Q3   Answer this question fully, including your main point, a quote and an explanation.

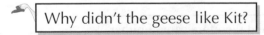

Why didn't the geese like Kit?

Q4   Read this review and answer the question to the right.

> Last night's performance of *The Tempest* was like a grand opera and a fireworks display rolled into one. Luke Matchett *lived* the role of Prospero and Frank Dunn's Caliban was suitably evil, whilst hinting at an underlying sadness. An absolute triumph!

How does the writer emphasise their opinion about the performance?

Use the ideas in Q1 and Q2 to help you plan your answer. Back up your answer with quotes and explanations.

Writing Your Answers

You're on your own now, sunshine. Well, not quite. You've got all these lovely questions here to keep you company. Lovely, lovely questions = lucky, lucky you. Don't forget to quote...

JULIET	What's in a name? That which we call a rose By any other word would smell as sweet; So Romeo would, were he not Romeo called, Retain that dear perfection which he owes Without that title. Romeo, doff thy name, And for thy name, which is no part of thee, Take all myself.
ROMEO	I take thee at thy word. Call me but love, and I'll be new baptised; Henceforth I never will be Romeo.
JULIET	What man art thou that thus bescreened in night So stumblest on my counsel?
ROMEO	By a name I know not how to tell thee who I am. My name, dear saint, is hateful to myself, Because it is an enemy to thee;

***Romeo and Juliet*, Act 2, Scene 2, lines 43-56**

Answer each question in turn. When you make a point, remember to back it up with a quote and explain how the point goes with your quote.

Q5 Write a short paragraph explaining what impression this extract gives you of Romeo and Juliet's relationship.

Q6 Sketch out the grid below, then fill it in with quotes to back up each point.

Point	Quote
Names play an important part in 'Romeo and Juliet'.	
Juliet wants Romeo to give up his name.	
Romeo hates his name.	
Juliet wasn't expecting to hear Romeo.	

Q7 What kind of atmosphere is there in this scene?

Don't answer back — always answer forwards...

So, that's the basics of how to answer the questions. The next few pages are about the different types of Shakespeare question you may come across. Fifteen pages of joy. Sigh.

What Characters Do

You'll probably have to get to grips with some questions about the characters. The best way to tackle these pesky blighters is to have a general look at what the characters <u>do</u>.

Q1 This is what the main characters get up to in the early scenes of *Romeo and Juliet*.

ROMEO

ACT 1 SCENE 5 Romeo and his friends break into the Capulets' party to try and find some girls. Romeo meets Juliet for the first time and it's love at first sight.

ACT 2 SCENE 2 Romeo climbs over the Capulets' wall to go and see Juliet. He declares his love for her.

JULIET

ACT 1 SCENE 3 Juliet finds out that Paris wants to marry her. She's not that bothered about marriage.

ACT 1 SCENE 5 Juliet meets Romeo and they kiss. She finds out that he's a Montague and she is devastated.

ACT 2 SCENE 2 Juliet talks about Romeo from her balcony. He appears and they say they love each other.

a) Write out at least **two** of the words or phrases below to describe each character.

romantic   unhappy   worried about family loyalty   useless

determined   rude   stupid   desirable   quick to fall in love

b) Write a sentence to explain why you've chosen each word or phrase.

Q2 Read this extract, then answer the questions.

> FRIAR LAWRENCE   Hold, daughter, I do spy a kind of hope,
> Which craves as desperate an execution
> As that is desperate which we would prevent.
> If, rather than to marry County Paris,
> Thou hast the strength of will to slay thyself,
> Then is it likely thou wilt undertake
> A thing like death to chide away this shame,
> That cop'st with Death himself to scape from it;
> And if thou dar'st, I'll give thee remedy.
>
> **Romeo and Juliet**, Act 4, Scene 1, lines 68-76

a) Write these sentences out in the order of the extract so they describe the Friar's plan.

"I've thought of a plan, but it's dangerous."   "...then you'd be prepared to face death if it solved your problem."

"If you are strong enough to die rather than marry Paris..."   "If you dare to do it, then I'll help."

b) Write a few sentences explaining what this extract tells you about Friar Lawrence's character.

What Characters Say

So, the first bit you need to include when you write about a character is what they do. The second but-still-just-as-important bit is the way they speak and how they treat other people.

Q1 These extracts are both from speeches Caliban makes in *The Tempest*.

> **A** This island's mine, by Sycorax my mother,
> Which thou tak'st from me. When thou cam'st first,
> Thou strok'st me and made much of me,
>   wouldst give me
> Water with berries in't, and teach me how
> To name the bigger light...
>
> **The Tempest**, Act 1, Scene 2, lines 333-337

> **B** Thou mak'st me merry. I am full of pleasure.
> Let us be jocund — will you troll the catch
> You taught me but whilere?
>
> **The Tempest**, Act 3, Scene 2, lines 116-118

a) Say which of the extracts each of these sentences is about.

> **Caliban says that he used to be treated better, and that rightfully the island is his.**
>
> **Caliban wants to have a party.**

b) Which speech shows Caliban thinks he owns the island? Explain why.

c) Which speech shows Caliban feels that he has been wronged? Explain why.

Q2 These two bits are from speeches made by Prospero in *The Tempest*.

> **A** A treacherous army levied, one midnight
> Fated to th' purpose, did Antonio open
> The gates of Milan, and i' th' dead of darkness,
> The ministers for th' purpose hurried thence
> Me and thy crying self.
>
> **The Tempest**, Act 1, Scene 2, lines 129-133

> **B** You, brother mine, that entertained ambition,
> Expelled remorse and nature, who, with Sebastian —
> Whose inward pinches therefore are most strong —
> Would here have killed your king, I do forgive thee,
> Unnatural though thou art.
>
> **The Tempest**, Act 5, Scene 1, lines 75-79

a) Say which of the extracts each of these sentences is about.

> **Prospero says he forgives Antonio and Sebastian for betraying him and plotting against Alonso.**
>
> **Prospero talks about how he and Miranda were banished from Milan.**

b) Write down **three** words that could describe Prospero as he appears in these quotes.

Q3 These words are spoken by Romeo towards the end of *Romeo and Juliet*.

> **A** How oft when men are at the point of death
> Have they been merry! Which their keepers call
> A lightning before death.
>
> *Romeo and Juliet*, Act 5, Scene 3, lines 88-90

> **B** Death, that hath sucked the honey of thy breath,
> Hath had no power yet upon thy beauty.
> Thou art not conquered.
>
> *Romeo and Juliet*, Act 5, Scene 3, lines 92-94

a) In your own words, write out what Romeo's saying in each speech.

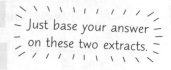

Just base your answer on these two extracts.

b) Write down at least **three** words you could use to describe Romeo.

What Characters Say

Almost everything a character says tells you a bit more about them.
Here's some more practice at working out what characters are like and writing about it.

Q4 Read the extract then answer the questions.

> ALONSO   You cram these words into mine ears against
> The stomach of my sense. Would I had never
> Married my daughter there, for, coming thence,
> My son is lost, and, in my rate, she too,
> Who is so far from Italy removed
> I ne'er again shall see her. O thou mine heir
> Of Naples and of Milan, what strange fish
> Hath made his meal on thee?
>
> ***The Tempest**, Act 2, Scene 1, lines 104-111*

King Alonso and his followers have just been washed up on an island after their ship was caught in a storm. Alonso fears his son Ferdinand is dead, but Gonzalo has been trying to comfort him.

a) Write out each of these comments about Alonso, along with the best explanation.

i) Alonso is pessimistic.	• **He's annoyed when people try to cheer him up.**
ii) Alonso feels guilty.	• **He blames himself for what's happened to Ferdinand.**
iii) Alonso is irritable.	• **He feels sure Ferdinand is dead.**

b) Write down a quote from the extract to back up each of the explanations from part **a)**.

Q5 Read the extract then answer the question.

> LADY CAPULET   Well, well, thou hast a careful father, child,
>   One who, to put thee from thy heaviness,
>   Hath sorted out a sudden day of joy,
>   That thou expects not, nor I looked not for.
> JULIET   Madam, in happy time, what day is that?
> LADY CAPULET   Marry, my child, early next Thursday morn,
>   The gallant, young, and noble gentleman,
>   The County Paris, at Saint Peter's Church,
>   Shall happily make thee there a joyful bride.
> JULIET   Now by Saint Peter's Church and Peter too,
>   He shall not make me there a joyful bride.
>
> ***Romeo and Juliet**, Act 3, Scene 5, lines 107-117*

Juliet is refusing to marry Paris, even though her father has secretly arranged a wedding to surprise her.

a) Write out each of these comments about the characters' feelings and match them with the best quote.

i)   Juliet has been feeling down recently.

ii) Juliet's dad has worked hard to get the wedding sorted quickly.

iii) Juliet is reluctant to marry Paris.

• **"thou hast a careful father, child, / One who... / Hath sorted out a sudden day of joy"**

• **"to put thee from thy heaviness"**

• **"He shall not make me there a joyful bride"**

What Characters Say

Q6 Read the text, then sketch out the table and fill in the missing explanations and quotes.

> FRIAR LAWRENCE   What, rouse thee, man! Thy Juliet is alive,
> For whose dear sake thou wast but lately dead;
> There art thou happy. Tybalt would kill thee,
> But thou slew'st Tybalt — there art thou happy.
> The law that threatened death becomes thy friend,
> And turns it to exile; there art thou happy:
> A pack of blessings lights upon thy back.
> Happiness courts thee in her best array,
> But, like a misbehavèd and sullen wench,
> Thou pout'st upon thy fortune and thy love:
> Take heed, take heed, for such die miserable.
>
> *Romeo and Juliet*, Act 3, Scene 3, lines 136-146

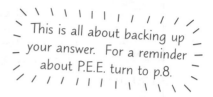
This is all about backing up your answer. For a reminder about P.E.E. turn to p.8.

Point	Quote	Explanation
Romeo is ungrateful for all the luck he's had.	"A pack of blessings lights upon thy back."	Friar Lawrence explains that Romeo should be glad to be alive and well.
Romeo has been saved from execution, even though he killed Tybalt.		
Romeo wanted to be dead for Juliet's sake.		

Q7 Read the extract below, then sketch a grid like the one from **Q6** and fill in as many comments, backed up by quotes and explanations, as you can.

> PROSPERO   Thou poisonous slave, got by the devil himself
> Upon thy wicked dam, come forth!
>
> *Enter* CALIBAN
>
> CALIBAN   As wicked dew as e'er my mother brushed
> With raven's feather from unwholesome fen
> Drop on you both! A south-west blow on ye
> And blister you all o'er!
>
> PROSPERO   For this, be sure, tonight thou shalt have cramps,
> Side-stitches that shall pen thy breath up, urchins
> Shall, for that vast of night that they may work,
> All exercise on thee, thou shalt be pinched
> As thick as honeycomb, each pinch more stinging
> Than bees that made 'em.

> CALIBAN   I must eat my dinner.
> This island's mine, by Sycorax my mother,
> Which thou tak'st from me. When thou cam'st first,
> Thou strok'st me and made much of me,
>   wouldst give me
> Water with berries in't, and teach me how
> To name the bigger light, and how the less,
> That burn by day and night, and then I loved thee,
> And showed thee all the qualities o'th'isle,
> The fresh springs, brine-pits, barren place and fertile.
> Cursed be I that did so! All the charms
> Of Sycorax, toads, beetles, bats, light on you!
>
> *The Tempest*, Act 1, Scene 2, lines 321-342

How Characters Think

Writing about __why__ characters do things will turn your Shakespeare work into top-notch stuff.

Q1   In this extract from *The Tempest*, Prospero gives his slave Caliban some instructions.

> PROSPERO   Hag-seed, hence!
> Fetch us in fuel. And be quick, thou 'rt best,
> To answer other business. Shrugg'st thou, malice?
> If thou neglect'st, or dost unwillingly
> What I command, I'll **rack** thee with old cramps,
> Fill all thy bones with aches, make thee roar,
> That beasts shall tremble at thy din.
>
> CALIBAN   No, pray thee.
> *(aside)* I must obey. His **art** is of such power,
> It would control my dam's god, **Setebos**,
> And make a **vassal** of him.
>
> **The Tempest**, Act 1, Scene 2, lines 367-376

rack = torture

art = magic
Setebos = an evil spirit
vassal = inferior person

a)   What does Prospero tell Caliban to do?

b)   Why does Prospero become annoyed with Caliban?

c)   Why does Caliban decide to do as he is told?

Q2   Below are three quotes (A-C) from Lord Capulet in *Romeo and Juliet*.
Match each one to the correct summary (**i-iii**).

A   I would not for the wealth of all this town
Here in my house do him disparagement;
Therefore be patient, take no note of him;
Romeo and Juliet, Act 1, Scene 5, lines 68-70

B   My sword, I say! Old Montague is come,
And flourishes his blade in spite of me.
Romeo and Juliet, Act 1, Scene 1, lines 69-70

C   Day, night, work, play,
Alone, in company, still my care hath been
To have her matched;
Romeo and Juliet, Act 3, Scene 5, lines 176-178

i)   Lord Capulet has been trying hard to find Juliet a husband.

ii)   Lord Capulet doesn't want to kick Romeo out of the party.

iii)   Lord Capulet wants to fight Lord Montague.

Q3   Read the extract from *The Tempest* then answer the questions below.

> PROSPERO   Thou most lying slave,
> Whom **stripes** may move, not kindness! I have used thee,
> Filth as thou art, with human care, and lodged thee
> In mine own cell, till thou didst seek to violate
> The honour of my child.
>
> **The Tempest**, Act 1, Scene 2, lines 346-350

stripes = whips

a)   What words suggest Caliban is badly treated?

b)   Why is Caliban no longer a friend of Prospero and Miranda?

Writing About Descriptions

You need to write about <u>how</u> Shakespeare describes things, not just re-tell the story. Sorry.

Q1 In this bit from *Romeo and Juliet,* Romeo talks about how he has had a dream that something bad is going to happen that evening.

> ROMEO   I fear, too early, for my mind misgives
> **Some consequence yet hanging in the stars**
> Shall bitterly begin his fearful date
> With this night's revels and expire the term
> Of a despisèd life closed in my breast,
> By some vile forfeit of untimely death.
> But **He**, that hath the steerage of my course,
> Direct my sail! On, lusty gentlemen.
>
> ***Romeo and Juliet,* Act 1, Scene 4, lines 106-113**

Some consequence yet
hanging in the stars = fate

He = God

a) Write these four lines out in the order they come in the scene.

   Let's get going.   God's in charge of my life, he'll do what he wants.

     Something big is going to happen tonight.   The party tonight will end badly.

b) Write down **two** phrases which show Romeo's feelings about the party.

c) Write down **one** phrase which shows Romeo's attitude to fate.

d) What is Romeo's reaction to his dream — what does he decide to do about it?

e) Write a mini-essay explaining how the language of this piece creates a feeling of tension in the scene. Include information from your answers to parts **a)** to **d)**.

Q2 Write a mini-essay explaining how the language in the extract from *Romeo and Juliet* below, creates a clear picture of the Montagues' and Capulets' past behaviour.

> PRINCE   Rebellious subjects, enemies to peace,
> Profaners of this neighbour-stainèd steel —
> Will they not hear? — What, ho! You men, you beasts!
> That quench the fire of your pernicious rage
> with purple fountains issuing from your veins,
> On pain of torture, from those bloody hands
> Throw your mistempered weapons to the ground,
> And hear the sentence of your movèd prince.
> Three civil brawls, bred of an airy word,
> By thee, old Capulet, and Montague,
> Have thrice disturbed the quiet of our streets,
> And made Verona's ancient citizens
> Cast by their grave beseeming ornaments,
> To wield old partisans, in hands as old.
>
> ***Romeo and Juliet,* Act 1, Scene 1, lines 73-86**

Don't forget P.E.E. —
make a point, back it
up with a quote, then
explain the quote.

Writing About Imagery

If you spot some imagery in a Shakespeare play, <u>definitely</u> mention it. It'll go down a treat.

Q1 For each extract below, answer the questions that follow.

> **A** FRIAR LAWRENCE   These violent delights have violent ends
> And in their triumph die, like fire and **powder**.
> *Romeo and Juliet*, Act 2, Scene 6, lines 9-10

powder = gunpowder

> **B** MERCUTIO   And thou make minstrels of us, look to hear nothing but discords.
> Here's my **fiddlestick**, here's that shall make you **dance**.
> *Romeo and Juliet*, Act 3, Scene 1, lines 42-45

fiddlestick = violin bow or sword

dance = dance or dodge

> **C** *Caliban, Stephano and Trinculo are driven out*
> PROSPERO   Go charge my goblins that they grind their joints
> With dry convulsions, shorten up their sinews
> With aged cramps, and more pinch-spotted make them
> Than **pard** or **cat o' mountain**.
> *The Tempest*, Act 4, Scene 1, lines 257-260

Prospero is telling Ariel to use magic to torment Caliban, Stephano and Trinculo.

pard = leopard
cat o' mountain = another word for leopard

a) What's being described in the image?

b) What's it being compared to?

c) What does the image tell you about the thing being described?

d) What does the image tell you about the character's thoughts or state of mind?

Q2 What effect do you think the imagery in this extract from *The Tempest* would have on an audience? Use parts **a)** to **d)** from above to help you plan your mini-essay.

> PROSPERO   In few, they hurried us aboard a **bark**,
> Bore us some leagues to the sea, where they prepared
> A rotten carcass of a butt, not **rigged**,
> Nor **tackle**, sail, nor mast. The very rats
> Instinctively have quit it. There they hoist us,
> To cry to th'sea, that roared to us, to sigh
> To th'winds, whose pity, sighing back again,
> Did us but loving wrong.
> *The Tempest*, Act 1, Scene 2, lines 145-152

bark = a kind of boat

rigged, tackle = sailing terms

Prospero was overthrown by Antonio as Duke of Milan. He and his daughter Miranda were dropped in the sea in a tiny, leaky boat and left to die. In this extract Prospero tells Miranda what happened.

Julie-ate her copy of the Shakespeare play...

Remember, if an extract contains a particular image, it's not there out of pure coincidence.
Try and think why Shakespeare included it and what effect he wanted it to have on the audience.

Writing About Mood

Mood is all about the atmosphere the language creates and how it makes the audience feel.

Q1 Read the extracts, then copy out the table headings below.
Fill in the table with notes for each of the extracts.

	Setting	How the characters speak	Description and imagery	Mood
A				

A CALIBAN   How does thy honour? Let me lick thy shoe.
           I'll not serve him — he is not valiant.
    TRINCULO Thou liest, most ignorant monster: I am in case to jostle a constable.
           Why, thou debauched fish, thou, was there ever man a coward that
           hath drunk so much sack as I today? Wilt thou tell a monstrous lie,
           being but half a fish and half a monster?
    CALIBAN   Lo, how he mocks me! Wilt thou let him, my lord?
    TRINCULO 'Lord' quoth he! That a monster should be such a **natural**!
    CALIBAN   Lo, lo again! Bite him to death, I prithee.

The Tempest, Act 3, Scene 2, lines 22-30

For each note you make, write a quote to show where you got your idea from.

natural = idiot

B JULIET   What devil art thou that dost torment me thus?
    This torture should be roared in dismal hell.
    Hath Romeo slain himself? Say thou but 'ay'
    And that bare vowel 'I' shall poison more
    Than the death-darting eye of **cockatrice**.
    I am not I, if there be such an 'ay',
    Or those eyes shut, that makes thee answer 'ay'.
    If he be slain, say 'ay', or if not, 'no':
    Brief sounds determine my **weal** or woe.

Romeo and Juliet, Act 3, Scene 2, lines 43-51

cockatrice = a mythical creature which killed with a look

weal = happiness

C MERCUTIO   Nay, I'll conjure too.
    Romeo! Humours! Madman! Passion! Lover!
    Appear thou in the likeness of a sigh,
    Speak but one rhyme, and I am satisfied.
    Cry but 'Ay me!' pronounce but 'love' and 'dove',
    Speak to my gossip Venus one fair word,
    One nickname for her **purblind** son and heir,
    Young Adam Cupid, he that shot so trim,
    When King Cophetua loved the beggar-maid!
    He heareth not, he stirreth not, he moveth not;
    The ape is dead, and I must conjure him.
    I conjure thee by Rosaline's bright eyes,
    By her high forehead and her scarlet lip,
    By her fine foot, straight leg and quivering thigh
    And the **demesnes** that there adjacent lie,
    That in thy likeness thou appear to us!

Romeo and Juliet, Act 2, Scene 1, lines 6-21

purblind = totally blind

demesnes = park land

Q2 Write a mini-essay on the mood in one of the extracts, using your notes from **Q1**.

Writing About Persuasive Language

Shakespeare's characters use persuasive language all the time — though it doesn't always go exactly to plan... If you spot some persuasive language, make sure you write about it.

Q1 Write down a quote from the extract to show where each of the persuading tricks is being used.

Antonio is trying to persuade Sebastian to kill Alonso and Gonzalo (Alonso's advisor) so that Sebastian can take Alonso's place as King of Naples.

> ANTONIO   Twenty consciences
> That stand 'twixt me and Milan, candied be they
> And melt, ere they molest! Here lies your brother,
> No better than the earth he lies upon,
> If he were that which now he's like — that's dead —
> Whom I with this obedient steel, three inches of it,
> Can lay to bed for ever, whiles you, doing thus,
> To the perpetual wink for aye might put
> This ancient morsel, this Sir Prudence, who
> Should not upbraid our course. For all the rest,
> They'll take suggestion as a cat laps milk,
> They'll tell the clock to any business that
> We say befits the hour.
>
> **The Tempest, Act 2, Scene 1, lines 277-289**

Persuading tricks

says it will be very simple to kill Alonso

laughs at the idea of feeling guilty

says Gonzalo won't be a problem

says no one else will stand in their way

Q2 Write down a quote from the extract to show where each of the persuading tricks is being used.

Juliet is telling the Nurse not to blame or hate Romeo, even though he has just killed Tybalt, Juliet's cousin, in a street fight.

> NURSE   Shame come to Romeo!
> JULIET   Blistered be thy tongue
> For such a wish! He was not born to shame:
> Upon his brow shame is ashamed to sit;
> For 'tis a throne where honour may be crowned
> Sole monarch of the universal earth.
> O what a beast I was to chide at him!
> NURSE   Will you speak well of him that killed your cousin?
> JULIET   Shall I speak ill of him that is my husband?
>
> **Romeo and Juliet, Act 3, Scene 2, lines 90-97**

Persuading tricks

stands up to insults

uses violent language to emphasise her emotions

uses romantic language

insists Romeo is honourable

uses rhetorical questions

Q3 Write a mini-essay on how persuasive tricks are used in one of the extracts above.

Performance — The Basics

Plays are meant to be performed. Sounds obvious, right? But it'll give your Shakespeare work a huge boost if you can write about how it could all look on stage.

Q1 Copy out all the bits of this extract where Prospero's talking to himself.

Prospero's decided to make things difficult for Ferdinand and Miranda, in order to test their love for each other.

> PROSPERO   Soft, sir, one word more!
> *(Aside)* They are both in either's pow'rs, but this swift business
> I must uneasy make, lest too light winning
> Make the prize light. *(To Ferdinand)* One word more — I charge thee
> That thou attend me — thou dost here usurp
> The name thou ow'st not and hast put thyself
> Upon this island as a spy, to win it
> From me, the lord on't.
> **The Tempest, Act 1, Scene 2, lines 452-459**

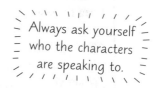

Always ask yourself who the characters are speaking to.

Q2 Which of the words on the right describe the way Prospero might talk when he's talking to himself?

thoughtful   loud

forceful   accusatory

angry   quiet

Q3 Which of the words on the right describe the way Prospero might talk when he's speaking to Ferdinand?

Q4 Explain how and why Romeo's feelings change during the following extract.

Romeo has broken into Juliet's tomb and intends to kill himself. Paris thinks Romeo caused her death, so he challenges him.

> ROMEO   I must indeed, and therefore came I hither.
>   Good gentle youth, tempt not a desperate man.
>   Fly hence, and leave me: think upon these gone.
>   Let them affright thee. I beseech thee, youth,
>   Put not another sin upon my head,
>   By urging me to fury. O, be gone!
>   By heaven, I love thee better than myself,
>   For I came hither armed against myself.
>   Stay not, be gone; live, and hereafter say,
>   A madman's mercy bade thee run away.
> PARIS   I do defy thy conjurations,
>   And apprehend thee for a felon here.
> ROMEO   Will thou provoke me? Then have at thee, boy!
> **Romeo and Juliet, Act 5, Scene 3, lines 58-70**

Characters' feelings often change <u>during</u> a scene.

Name a smoothie playwright — milkshakespeare...
You probably say different things to your mates than you do to your parents. That's why you need to keep track of who's speaking to who in a scene, and how they might be feeling at the time.

How Characters Speak

You need to think about how the characters should <u>sound</u> — what tone of voice they should use, how loudly and how fast they should speak — that sort of thing. It's all very dramatic.

Q1 Read the passage below. For each of the parts in bold, explain how you think the speaker feels and how they might speak the words.

LADY CAPULET   He is a kinsman to the Montague,
Affection makes him false, he speaks not true:
Some twenty of them fought in this black strife,
And all those twenty could but kill one life.
I beg for justice, which thou, Prince, must give:
Romeo slew Tybalt, **Romeo must not live.**

PRINCE   Romeo slew him, he slew Mercutio;
Who now the price of his dear blood doth owe?

MONTAGUE   Not Romeo, Prince, he was
                              Mercutio's friend;
His fault concludes but what the law should end,
The life of Tybalt.

PRINCE   And for that offence
Immediately we do exile him hence.
I have an interest in your hearts' proceeding;
My blood for your rude brawls doth lie a-bleeding;
But I'll amerce you with so strong a fine
That you shall all repent the loss of mine.
I will be deaf to pleading and excuses,
No tears nor prayers shall purchase out abuses.
Therefore use none. Let Romeo hence in haste,
Else, when he is found, that hour is his last.
Bear hence this body, and attend our will:
Mercy but murders, pardoning those that kill.

Romeo and Juliet, Act 3, Scene 1, lines 171-192

There's no right or wrong answer to this question.

Q2 Suggest how the actor playing Prospero could speak the lines below to emphasise his feelings to the audience.

PROSPERO   O good Gonzalo,
My true preserver, and a loyal sir
To him thou follow'st! I will pay thy graces
Home both in word and deed. Most cruelly
Didst thou, Alonso, use me and my daughter.
Thy brother was a furtherer in the act. —
Thou art pinched for't now, Sebastian. — Flesh and blood,
You, brother mine, that entertained ambition,
Expelled remorse and nature, who, with Sebastian —
Whose inward pinches therefore are most strong —
Would here have killed your king, I do forgive thee,
Unnatural though thou art. Their understanding
Begins to swell, and the approaching tide
Will shortly fill the reasonable shore
That now lies foul and muddy. Not one of them
That yet looks on me, or would know me. Ariel,
Fetch me the hat and **rapier** in my cell.

The Tempest, Act 5 Scene 1, lines 68-84

Detailed answers are so much better. General wishy-washy ones are... worse.

rapier = a type of sword

How Characters Move

Another part of thinking about performance is how characters <u>move</u>. Movements can emphasise what the characters say, and how they react to other characters. It also stops pins and needles.

Read the extract on the right and answer the question.

Q1   Write out all the bits that could tell you how the characters could move, and describe the movements.

PROSPERO	The fringed curtains of thine eye advance,
	And say what thou seest yond.
MIRANDA	What is't? A spirit?
	Lord, how it looks about! Believe me, sir,
	It carries a brave form. But 'tis a spirit.
PROSPERO	No, wench — it eats and sleeps and hath such senses
	As we have, such. This gallant which thou seest
	Was in the wreck, and but he's something stained
	With grief, that's beauty's canker, thou mightst call him
	A goodly person. He hath lost his fellows,
	And strays about to find 'em.

The Tempest, Act 1, Scene 2, lines 411-420

Q2   Write down ideas for how each of the characters could speak and move in these lines.

JULIET	Good pilgrim, you do wrong your hand too much,
	Which mannerly devotion shows in this,
	For saints have hands that pilgrims' hands do touch,
	And palm to palm is holy palmers' kiss.
ROMEO	Have not saints lips, and holy palmers too?
JULIET	Ay, pilgrim, lips that they must use in prayer.
ROMEO	O then, dear saint, let lips do what hands do:
	They pray — grant thou, lest faith turn to despair.
JULIET	Saints do not move, though grant for prayers' sake.
ROMEO	Then move not while my prayer's effect I take.
	Thus from my lips, by thine, my sin is purged.
	Kissing her

Romeo and Juliet, Act 1, Scene 5, lines 96-106

Romeo is chatting up Juliet at the Capulet family party.

Q3   Write down any bits in the following extract where characters could emphasise their feelings through their movements, and suggest what those movements could be.

PROSPERO	*(Aside)* I had forgot that foul conspiracy
	Of the beast Caliban and his confederates
	Against my life. The minute of their plot
	Is almost come. *(To the spirits)* Well done!
	Avoid — no more!
	(The spirits depart)
FERDINAND	This is strange. Your father's in some passion
	That works him strongly.
MIRANDA	Never till this day
	Saw I him touched with anger so distempered.

The Tempest, Act 4, Scene 1, lines 139-145

Prospero has just remembered Caliban's plot against him and broken off the masque to celebrate Ferdinand and Miranda's engagement.

In this extract the movements are probably going to be quite subtle. Think about facial expressions as well as big movements.

Section Five — Shakespeare

Themes in 'Romeo and Juliet'

Themes are the big ideas that a play is about. If you're ever asked to write about themes, you'll have to say (and show) how a certain bit of text relates to one of the main themes.

Q1   This extract deals with the themes of love and family loyalty.
Answer the questions below that ask about these themes:

> JULIET   'Tis but thy name that is my enemy —
> Thou art thyself, though not a Montague.
> What's Montague? It is nor hand nor foot,
> Nor arm nor face, nor any other part
> Belonging to a man. O be some other name!
> What's in a name? That which we call a rose
> By any other word would smell as sweet;
> So Romeo would, were he not Romeo called,
> Retain that dear perfection which he owes
> Without that title. Romeo, **doff** thy name,
> And for thy name, which is no part of thee,
> Take all myself.
>
> ***Romeo and Juliet**, Act 2, Scene 2, lines 38-49*

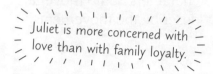
Juliet is more concerned with love than with family loyalty.

doff = take off

a)   Write out all the parts of the speech that mention names.

b)   Write down what each part means.

c)   In your opinion, what does Juliet think about names?

d)   What do you think Shakespeare is telling the audience about names in this speech?

Q2   What different ideas about life and death does Shakespeare present in the speech below? Ask yourself questions like **a)-d)** above to help you plan your answer.

> ROMEO   What less than doomsday is the Prince's doom?
> LAWRENCE   A gentler judgement vanished from his lips,
>   Not body's death, but body's banishment.
> ROMEO   Ha, banishment! Be merciful, say 'death';
>   For exile hath more terror in his look,
>   Much more than death. Do not say 'banishment'.
> LAWRENCE   Hence from Verona art thou banishèd:
>   Be patient, for the world is broad and wide.
> ROMEO   There is no world without Verona walls,
>   But purgatory, torture, hell itself.
>   Hence 'banishèd' is banished from the world,
>   And world's exile is death: then banishèd
>   Is death mistermed. Calling death 'banishèd',
>   Thou cut'st my head off with a golden axe,
>   And smilest upon the stroke that murders me.
>
> ***Romeo and Juliet**, Act 3, Scene 3, lines 9-23*

Themes in 'The Tempest'

The Tempest is all about fate, justice, forgiveness, freedom, magic, slavery... not much to cover, then. Anyway, here's some more practice on questions dealing with themes.

Q1 Read the extract below and then answer the questions about justice in *The Tempest*.

> ARIEL   you three
> From Milan did supplant good Prospero,
> Exposed unto the sea, which hath **requit** it,
> Him, and his innocent child, for which foul deed
> The pow'rs, delaying, not forgetting, have
> Incensed the seas and shores, yea, all the creatures,
> Against your peace. Thee of thy son, Alonso,
> They have **bereft**, and do pronounce by me
> Ling'ring **perdition**, worse than any death
> Can be at once, shall step by step attend
> You and your ways, whose wraths to guard you from —
> Which here, in this most desolate isle, else falls
> Upon your heads — is nothing but heart's sorrow,
> And a clear life ensuing.

requit = avenged

bereft = deprived, taken

perdition = loss, ruin

The Tempest, Act 3, Scene 3, lines 69-82

a) Write out all the parts of the speech that are about justice.

b) Write down what each one means in your own words.

c) Write down what you think Ariel is saying about justice.

d) What do you think Shakespeare thinks about justice?

Q2 What different ideas about forgiveness does Shakespeare present in the speech below? Ask yourself questions like **a)-d)** above to help you plan your answer.

> ARIEL   Him you termed, sir, 'the good old lord, Gonzalo'.
> His tears run down his beard, like winter's drops
> From eaves of reeds. Your charm so strongly works 'em
> That if you now beheld them your affections
> Would become tender.
> PROSPERO   Dost thou think so, spirit?
> ARIEL   Mine would, sir, were I human.
> PROSPERO   And mine shall.
> Hast thou, which art but air, a touch, a feeling
> Of their afflictions, and shall not myself,
> One of their kind, that relish all as sharply,
> Passion as they, be kindlier moved than thou art?

> Though with their high wrongs I am struck to th'
>   quick,
> Yet with my nobler reason 'gainst my fury
> Do I take part. The rarer action is
> In virtue than in vengeance. They being penitent,
> The sole drift of my purpose doth extend
> Not a frown further. Go release them, Ariel.
> My charms I'll break, their senses I'll restore,
> And they shall be themselves.

The Tempest, Act 5, Scene 1, lines 15-32

Section Five — Shakespeare

Themes

Hurrah, the final Shakespeare questions! Here's some more theme practice to finish with.

Q1   Another key idea in *Romeo and Juliet* is hatred and the feud between the two families.

> SAMPSON   Draw, if you be men. Gregory,
> remember thy **washing** blow.
> > *They fight*
> BENVOLIO   Part, fools!
> Put up your swords — you know not what you do.
> > *Beats down their swords*
> > *Enter* TYBALT
> TYBALT   What, art thou drawn among these
> > heartless **hinds**?
> Turn thee, Benvolio, look upon thy death.

washing = slashing

> BENVOLIO   I do but keep the peace. Put up thy sword,
> Or manage it to part these men with me.
> TYBALT   What, drawn, and talk of peace! I hate the word,
> As I hate hell, all Montagues, and thee:
> Have at thee, coward!
> > *They fight*
> > *Enter several of both houses, who join the fray.*
> > *Then enter three or four CITIZENS with clubs*
> FIRST CITIZEN   **Clubs, bills, and partisans**!
> Strike! Beat them down! Down with the
> Capulets! Down with the Montagues!

***Romeo and Juliet**, Act 1, Scene 1, lines 54-66*

hinds = female deer

clubs, bills, and partisans = types of weapon

a)   Write out all the parts of this extract that make reference to hatred and the feud between the two families.

b)   Write down what each one means in your own words.

c)   Write down what you think Tybalt's attitude towards the Montagues is.

d)   What do you think Shakespeare is telling us about the feud in this extract?

Q2   What different ideas about the struggle for power between masters and servants does Shakespeare present in the passage below? Ask yourself questions like **a)-d)** above to help you plan your answer.

> CALIBAN   I must eat my dinner.
> This island's mine, by Sycorax my mother,
> Which thou tak'st from me. When thou cam'st first,
> **Thou strok'st me and made much of me**, wouldst give me
> Water with berries in't, and **teach me how**
> **To name the bigger light, and how the less**,
> That burn by day and night, and then I loved thee,
> And showed thee all the qualities o' th' isle,
> The fresh springs, brine-pits, barren place and fertile.

Thou strok'st me and made much
  of me = You took care of me

Teach me how / To name the bigger light, and how
  the less = taught me about the sun and the moon

sty me = keep me

> Cursed be I that did so! All the charms
> Of Sycorax, toads, beetles, bats, light on you!
> For I am all the subjects that you have,
> Which first was mine own king, and here you **sty me**
> In this hard rock, whiles you do keep from me
> The rest o' th' island.
> PROSPERO   Thou most lying slave,
> Whom **stripes** may move, not kindness! I have used thee,
> Filth as thou art, with human care, and lodged thee
> In mine own cell

***The Tempest**, Act 1, Scene 2, lines 332-349*

stripes = strikes with a whip

Planning Your Answer

Your work should always be carefully planned. This will allow you to structure your writing into clear paragraphs and help you to cover everything that you want to say. Splendid.

Q1   Copy out the following points from this story plan in the correct order:

i)   The wolf reveals who he is and tries to eat Red Riding Hood.

ii)   Red Riding Hood goes through the woods, meets the wolf, and tells him where she's going.

iii)   Red Riding Hood arrives at her grandma's house. She notices Grandma's strange appearance.

iv)   They all live happily ever after.

v)   The woodcutter hears Red Riding Hood shouting for help. He kills the wolf and rescues Grandma.

vi)   The wolf goes to Grandma's house. He locks Grandma in the cupboard and disguises himself by wearing Grandma's nightclothes.

vii)   Red Riding Hood's mother sends her to take some shopping to her grandma, but she warns her to ignore strangers, especially the wolf.

Q2   Imagine you need to write a news report about what happens in another fairy tale, for example 'Goldilocks and the Three Bears'. List the key things that you want to include in your report (try to keep to around seven or eight points).

Q3   Using the list you wrote for **Q2**, number the points in your list to show the order you have chosen for your report.

Q4   Now write your report. Write one paragraph for every point in your plan and make sure you have a clear concluding paragraph. Use the checklist below to help you.

Checklist
a) Write a paragraph about the first point on your list. Time yourself to ensure you don't take longer than five minutes.
b) Now re-read your first paragraph. Are you happy with it? If not, change it.
c) Once you are happy, move on to the next point in your list...
d) Repeat until you have covered everything on the list.
e) Re-read your completed article. Are you happy with it? If not, change the bits you dislike to complete your article.

Decide the order — hamburger, fries and a milkshake...

Planning your writing (munch) ensures you don't forget to (slurp) include anything. Start each point in your writing (munch munch) with a new paragraph to give it structure. (Mmm, this _is_ a tasty burger...)

Writing Essays

Essays aren't scary — and if you can answer these questions you can start feeling confident that you know just how to handle one. Hurrah.

> The smell their drummer made on-stage really put us off the gig. I told him we wouldn't bother seeing them again. In fact, I told them I'd tell everyone else I knew with tickets not to bother. They used to be my favourite band, but they're not now — they haven't been since last year.

Q1 Write out the following statements which apply to the above passage:

i) There is no introduction.

ii) It doesn't explain who the band are, or give any other context.

iii) It just trails off without a conclusion.

iv) There is a clear structure.

Q2 Write out the following sentences which could be included in a formal essay about someone's favourite band:

i) My favourite heavy metal band, "Orange Hamster" (formed in 1989), are as popular today as they ever were.

  ii) The O' Hamster have been kicking around for about 25 years now, and they're still packing them in at every gig.

iii) "Grannyknot" are rubbish — they can't play and the lead singer's as dull as dishwater.

  iv) "Grannyknot" are a band that I strongly dislike. They have very little musical talent, and their lead singer is painfully average.

v) My favourite musical genre is 60s rhythm and blues.

  vi) The best stuff around is old-time R&B.

Q3 Write down a bullet point list about what music you like and dislike, favourite bands, etc.

Q4 Using the points you wrote for **Q3** as a plan, write a formal mini-essay about your own musical tastes. Include your favourite band and favourite song (or songs). The essay should be written in paragraphs and include an introduction and a conclusion.

Essay writing — it's not rocket science... (that's aerospace engineering)

What you want for your essay (what you really, really want) is a good clear structure. If you nail that, and then crack out some top-class formal writing as well, you're on to a winner. Hurrah.

Writing Stories

Writing stories is a skill that improves with practice. These questions should help you get one step closer to writing that best-selling novel you've always wanted to write.

Q1 A good story follows a good structure. Put these parts of a story in the right order.

   i) a satisfying ending which ties up all the loose ends

   ii) a gripping opening to the story

   iii) an exciting development in the plot

Q2 Choose any **three** types of fiction below and write your own opening sentences to a story. Make sure that they grab the reader's attention.

   i) horror   **iii)** fairy tale   **v)** science fiction

   ii) adventure   **iv)** crime   **vi)** historical

Q3 Rewrite the following sentences, in at least **two** different ways, so that they grab the reader's attention. The first one has been done for you.

   a) The woman opened the door to the cellar.

      a) **Trembling with fear, the woman slowly pulled open the door to the dark cellar.**

          Unaware of the horrors that awaited her, the woman flung open the door to the cellar.

   b) The soldiers sat scared in the trenches.

   c) The spaceship was flying towards the planet.

   d) She thought she heard footsteps so she looked behind her.

   e) The avalanche headed for the climbers.

Q4 Match the following poor endings with a more interesting alternative from the box:

   a) They won the battle.   **d)** They sailed off into the sunset.

   b) They were together again at last.   **e)** They never caught the monster.

   c) The storm ended.   **f)** The innocent man was released.

> They were together again at last, but for how long?
> He had always insisted that he didn't do it; now, finally, justice had been done.
> "You will never defeat me!" cackled the vampire, and vanished into the darkness.
> The boat, silhouetted against the sunset, carried the two lovers to their destiny.
> After days of struggle, the exhausted soldiers were finally victorious.
> The streets were flooded and fallen trees lined the road, but at last it was over.

Writing to Inform, Explain and Advise

Informing, explaining and advising — basically, telling the reader some information.

Q1   Decide whether each of the texts below informs,
explains or advises. Explain your answer.

a)   A fact-file about deadly plant species.

b)   A pamphlet that suggests different things you could do to save water at home.

c)   A letter from the council with details about a new leisure centre.

d)   An email that points out why the school library has been closed.

e)   An article that tells you why fizzy drinks are bad for your health.

f)   A leaflet from the doctor's which recommends things
you can do to avoid catching the flu.

Q2   These three texts are all about swimming. Write down whether the purpose
of each text is to inform, explain or advise, and explain how you can tell.

> 1)   Swimming is by far my favourite sport. It's great exercise, especially for improving
> your strength. Swimming is also really convenient, as I can do it at any time of
> year. Because it's indoors, I never have to worry about swimming practice being
> cancelled because of bad weather. Finally, swimming is loads of fun! Swimming as
> part of a club is great way to make friends and take part in competitions.

> 2)   Humans have been swimming since prehistoric times, but it only became
> a popular competitive sport during the 1800s. At this time, British
> swimmers usually swam breaststroke. They only discovered front crawl
> in the mid 1800s when Native American swimmers, who had used front
> crawl for many years, beat them dramatically in a swimming competition.

> 3)   If you're thinking about taking up swimming regularly, it's a good idea to
> invest in a good pair of goggles. Not only will you be able to see where you're
> going, but you'll reduce the chances of picking up an eye infection in the
> pool. It's also worthwhile getting a swimming hat. It might not look very
> fashionable, but a hat will make you more streamlined and therefore faster.

Q3   Write two paragraphs about your favourite sport. Explain why you like it.

Writing to Inform, Explain and Advise

Whether you're writing to inform, explain or advise, you need
to make sure that your writing is clear and easy to understand.

Q4 Write out the points below that you would include
in an informative leaflet for Pizerrella's Pizzeria.

i) Pizerrella's Pizzeria first opened its doors in 2003, and has been offering
both sit-in and take-away services to local customers ever since.

   ii) The modern pizza was first invented in Naples, Italy.

iii) The pizzeria serves up a wide range of pizzas, including the Vesuvius,
with hot chilli, and the Liechtenstein, with frankfurter sausage.

   iv) When placing an order, we suggest that you try a delicious starter,
such as our gorgeous garlic bread or our fabulous cheese fritters.

v) Pizarrella's Pizzeria is open from 5 pm to 10.30 pm Monday
to Thursday, and 12 noon to 12 midnight Friday to Sunday.

   vi) Personally, my favourite pizza is the Paris pizza, which
comes topped with crispy frogs' legs. Delicious!

Q5 If you are writing to offer someone advice, you should give suggestions, not commands.
Change the following commands into suggestions. The first one has been done for you.

a) **e.g.** You must do what the teacher says.
It would be a good idea to do what the teacher says.

b) You have to take part in the race.

c) Leave your job.

d) Come swimming at the leisure centre tomorrow.

e) Make your mind up.

I suggest that you leave the pool now.

Q6 Imagine you are writing for a problem page in a magazine. You receive this letter:

> *I've just moved schools and I'm really struggling to settle in.*
> *What can I do to make friends?*
> *Yours lonesomely,*
> *Nat x*

Write a reply to Nat giving some friendly advice.

Advise, inform, explain — is this becoming a pain?

Get the difference between texts that inform, explain and advise crystal clear. Then, when you
write them yourself, you know exactly what you're aiming for, and the whole thing's a breeze...

Formal and Informal Letters

Depending on the kind of letter you're writing, you'll need to use formal or informal language.

Q1 Copy out the table below. Put each word, **a)-j)**, in the correct column.
After you've done this, complete the table by filling in the remaining blanks.
The first one has been done for you.

a) isn't
b) wasn't
c) goodbye
d) moreover
e) kids
f) reprimand
g) ensure
h) stuff
i) nevertheless
j) fab

	More formal	Less formal
a)	is not	isn't
b)		
c)		
d)		
e)		
f)		
g)		
h)		
i)		
j)		

Q2 Copy out the more formal sentence from each pair:

a) We would be most interested to hear your thoughts.
Let us know what you think.

b) It'll be really tough to win stuff on sports day.
The competition at this year's sports day is fierce.

c) Loads of people have mobile phones these days.
The number of people owning mobile phones continues to rise.

d) You are requested to contact Ms Pieterson for further details.
Get in touch with Ms Pieterson to find out more.

e) Shop shut tomorrow.
Customers are advised that SpeedyMart will be closed tomorrow.

Q3 Read this extract from a letter, written to a local MP.

> The pigeons, which invaded the church steeple two months ago, are really annoying. For starters, they squawk all the time, so you can't hear yourself think, let alone hear the First Soprano. Plus, we have to put up with bird poo in the choir stalls. It really is too much to bear.

Write out the letter in full, replacing the informal words and phrases in the extract with more formal ones. Make sure you lay out your writing as you would in a letter.

Formal and Informal Letters

More questions on letter writing. Don't worry, I'm not expecting a thank you card...

Q4　Write out this formal letter, filling in the gaps using the words or phrases from the pairs below.

Dear Mr Brown,

.... for your letter.

.... sorry to hear that you .... enjoy your meal. .... you would have enjoyed something from our à la carte menu. .... a voucher which will .... a .... meal at any of our restaurants.

Yours sincerely,

A. J. Spudwrangler, for Spudwrangler Restaurants.

I'm sending you / Please find enclosed	Maybe / Perhaps	Thank you / Thanks
entitle you to / give you　　didn't / did not	I'm / I am	free / complimentary

Q5　Rewrite the formal letter below as an informal letter.

The Grange
Oxton
LH4 8PW

The Old Coach House
Bowden
RH3 7RL

Dear Josephine Baker,

　I am writing to ask your advice on a rather personal matter. Since I was young, I have enjoyed gymnastics, and had hoped to continue taking part in this sport for the rest of my life.

　Recently, however, I have started to suffer from rheumatism, which I believe is common among people of my advanced years.

　I have heard that, before you retired, you spent some years as a homoeopathist. Do you have any recommendations for herbal remedies which might ease my pain, and enable me to backflip again? Any advice would be gratefully received.

Yours sincerely,
Bessie Smith

Q6　Read the newspaper article below, and write a letter from Sterling Hayden to his daughter describing the events. Remember that it is an informal letter.

Sea Captain Reveals His Salsa Hell

A lone yachtsman was unable to land on shore for three months, because of his newly-developed addiction to salsa dancing. Wizened former-sea-captain Sterling Hayden told this newspaper that he had first started dancing when he watched a salsa-based exercise DVD his daughter lent him to help him keep in shape.

Says Sterling, "At first it was fun; I enjoyed tapping my toes. But soon I was addicted to salsa. I couldn't steer or keep course because the urge to dance was so strong. After three months, I finally recovered after finding a Mozart CD under a life jacket."

Writing to Persuade and Argue

Persuading and arguing is about getting someone else to agree with your point of view.

Q1 Which of the following are tricks you can use to make your writing more persuasive? Choose one or more from options **i)-v)** and write them down.

   i) Keep your writing polite. Don't intentionally offend people who disagree with your views.

   ii) Use humour, contrast and repetition to put people off your main point.

   iii) Use descriptive words to emphasise your points.

   iv) Get the reader on your side by saying "us" and "we".

   v) Back up your points with elephants.

Q2 Rewrite the following sentences, changing the language to make them sound less vague and more convincing.

   a) People should maybe think about the effect smoking could have on their health.

   b) One question we might ask is, "If the government have evidence about why we should eat spinach, would they mind sharing it with us?"

   c) If you don't want to go on the trip, it's probably best if you ask your mother to write a letter to the teacher explaining why.

Q3 Using adjectives makes your writing more persuasive, and adjectives work really well in groups of three. Copy down the sentences and fill in the blanks with adjectives.

   e.g. **We need to keep the local park; it is <u>peaceful</u>, <u>beautiful</u> and <u>unique</u>.**

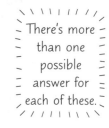

There's more than one possible answer for each of these.

   a) I enjoy swimming because it is relaxing, fun and ....

   b) It's important to read the newspapers because they are thought-provoking, ... and ....

   c) We all know that homework is .... , ... and ....

Q4 Copy out the following sentences, underlining the parts where you think the author is trying to be persuasive.

   a) How can you allow these poor, desperate people to go without food for any longer?

   b) Some people are living in a fantasy world and don't know how normal people live. They seem to think that everyone has enough money to spend on whatever they please.

   c) Their team is disorganised, unmotivated and unprepared.

   d) If you love theme parks as much as we do, we know that you'll have the time of your life here at Dizzyworld — you'll never want to leave!

Writing to Persuade and Argue

You can't ignore other people's points of view. To argue that your opinion is right, you need to say why other opinions are wrong — without getting rude or personal.

Q5 Are the following paragraphs persuasive, or not? Explain each of your answers.

a) You could vote for Claire Harris if you want to see an improvement in employment and a clamping down on crime in the local area. She introduced the Young Offenders Scheme. On the other hand, you could vote for Edward Jones. He has agreed to increase spending on health and education.

b) You should vote for Claire Harris because she is intelligent, honest and cares about the local area. Her scheme to help young offenders back into employment has been a major success and is the envy of other constituencies. People backing Edward Jones forget the appalling crime and unemployment rates which this constituency suffered the last time he was in power.

Q6 Use the evidence from the boxes below to make two properly backed-up paragraphs, following on from the opening lines **a)** and **b)**.

a) The death penalty should not be reintroduced in Britain.

b) The death penalty should be reintroduced in Britain.

Keeping people in prison costs the government money — on buildings, staff, food and healthcare. People who have committed horrific crimes and are sentenced to life imprisonment are wasting government resources.

Reintroducing the death penalty would also act as a deterrent to criminals. It would show them that the legal system in Britain is strong and it won't let them get away lightly with their crimes.

Lord Justice Hodgeman has said on this issue, "Although I have great faith in the British legal system, we should not lie to ourselves that it is infallible."

There have been several recent cases in Britain where long-serving prisoners have been found innocent because of new evidence. If we had the death penalty in Britain, these people would have been wrongly executed long ago.

Q7 Write a short article for your school newsletter arguing **either** that cars should be allowed in the school playground **or** that cars should be banned from the school playground. Mention all of the points from the table below in your article.

Why Cars Should be Allowed in the Playground	Why Cars Shouldn't be Allowed in the Playground
It's hard for teachers to find other parking nearby.	They increase the amount of noise outside school.
It's the safest place for teachers to leave their cars.	Children might be run over and injured or killed.
As long as people drive slowly it should be safe.	There will be less space for children to play and exercise.

Structuring Your Writing — Introductions

The introduction to a piece of writing is dead important. If your intro is no good, then people might think that the rest of your writing won't be great either.

Q1 Pretend you're writing a speech to give to the Parent-Teacher Association of your school. Which of the following words and phrases, **i)-x)**, would be good to use in your introduction?

i) Good morrow fair gentlemen

ii) Good evening

iii) Okey-dokey

iv) We are here tonight to discuss

v) We are here tonight to rant about

vi) In my introduction to this essay

vii) Hi, it's darn good you could all come tonight

viii) Welcome

ix) In conclusion

x) The key issue I am going to discuss is

Q2 In a persuasive essay you need to make sure your argument is clear in the introduction. Which of these introductions does this better? Explain why.

i)
> The issue of security is important in modern schools. Tragedies have taken place when violent outsiders have been able to walk unchallenged into school grounds. If security isn't improved in all schools, we have to ask ourselves: how long will it be before another tragedy happens?

ii)
> The issue of security is important in modern schools. A lot of schools have increased security since a series of violent incidents over the last few years. Some people think this is the right course of action to protect children. Others believe it creates an unhealthy atmosphere of fear and paranoia.

Q3 Below are an author's notes for the introduction of a story called 'Dancing Bob'. Use the information below to write an introduction to the story.

What happens	How it should feel
• Bob is getting ready for a night out	Happy, lighthearted
• He turns on some funky tunes	
• He opens his wardrobe — all his clothes have been torn to shreds	dramatic, surprising
• Bob hears a noise downstairs	scary — what's going to happen next?

Q4 Read this introduction to an essay about someone's favourite book. Explain why this introduction is not very engaging.

> I want to talk about my favourite book which is called 'Treasure Island'. It's about a boy and a treasure map and some pirates. It's pretty good, so I think you should probably read it.

Structuring Your Writing — Introductions

Sometimes it's best to start a piece of writing by telling 'em what you're going to tell 'em.

Q5 Which of the following introductions (**i-iii**) signpost clearly what the structure of the leaflet is going to be? Explain how.

i Schools can help the environment; a few simple things can make a big difference. We all know that recycling is important, but so are many other issues, for example educating children about the environment. This leaflet is all about how you can make your school environmentally friendly.

ii Schools can help the environment; a few simple things can make a big difference. This leaflet provides information about some easy steps schools can take. Three main areas are covered: recycling and reusing materials, school bus services and educating pupils about the environment.

iii Schools can help the environment, for example by recycling and reusing materials in class. This is very easy to do — try turning a painting over and doing another on the back. Simple! This leaflet will give you loads of other hints for making your school a greener place.

Q6 Signposting the structure of an essay is good, because it lets the reader know what to expect. Write out the phrases and sentences below that would be useful for this.

i) The main argument in favour of this will appear somewhere in this essay.

ii) The second half of this essay will discuss the disadvantages...

iii) Without a doubt, nothing can be done about this situation.

iv) There are three main issues at stake here; they will be discussed in turn.

v) The first half of this essay will discuss the advantages...

vi) The second reason for supporting this point of view...

vii) Finally, this essay will consider the impact on...

viii) This is a controversial topic.

Q7 Below is part of an essay plan. It's for an essay explaining why the writer likes going on holiday to the Lake District.

Paragraph 1: Beautiful scenery e.g. lakes, mountains, valleys, pretty villages

Paragraph 2: Lots of outdoors activities e.g. walking, climbing, kayaking

Paragraph 3: Fun things to visit e.g. aquarium, wild animal park, pencil museum

Write an introduction for this essay, signposting all of these points.

Structuring Your Writing — The Middle Bit

Once you've got your intro sorted, you need to structure your middle paragraphs.

Q1 The boxes **i)-vi)** below summarise the types of paragraphs in a typical persuasive essay. Put **i)-vi)** into a logical order and write them out.

i) Give a reason to support your argument. Back it up with evidence.

ii) Conclusion — bring together main points why your argument's right.

iii) Give a reason why people might not agree with your argument. Give evidence of why they are wrong.

iv) Give a second reason why people might not agree with your argument. Give evidence of why they are wrong.

v) Introduction — outline your main argument.

vi) Give a second reason to support your argument. Back it up with evidence.

Q2 Look at the plan below. Write the first sentence for each of the main paragraphs.

> **Why we should do more sports in school**
>
> <u>Intro</u>
> **Paragraph 1:** Sports keep people fit and healthy.
> **Paragraph 2:** Sports help develop team skills.
> **Paragraph 3:** There are loads of sports to choose from, so there's bound to be something for everyone.
> <u>Conclusion</u>

Q3 Write down the correct chronological order for these paragraphs.

Chronological — in the order in which things happened.

i) We now know that the golden death mask Schliemann found in *Grave Circle A* is unlikely to belong to Agamemnon. The graves date from c.1500 BC, while the Trojan War probably happened in 1200-1100 BC.

ii) The ruined cities of Tiryns, Mycenae and Pylos, in Greece, date from as far back as 1500 BC. They are mentioned in Homer's epic poems 'The Iliad' and 'The Odyssey'. For example, the character Agamemnon in 'The Iliad' is called the ruler of Mycenae.

iii) The ruins of Mycenae were excavated by the German archaeologist Heinrich Schliemann in the nineteenth century. He was a romantic man. When he found a golden death mask in Grave Circle A at Mycenae, he claimed that he had "seen the face of Agamemnon".

iv) Further excavations are still happening at Mycenae. Archaeologists want to find out more about ancient Mycenean religions; evidence so far includes frescoes, shrines and statues of goddesses. How much more can they find in the ruins of this great city?

Structuring Your Writing — The Middle Bit

When you've got a long piece of writing to do, always make sure you sketch out a plan first. That way you can work out the best way to order your writing before you start.

Q4 Read the following notice.

> Beanthwaite High School Athletics Club
>
> ## Last Night Out Before Training
>
> <u>For the attention of athletics club members</u>:
>
> The club has decided to pay for a free meal out on the eve of the training period for the County Athletics Championships.
> The club coach urges students to remember that:
> • the championships will soon be upon us
> • all their hard work will be rewarded with good performances
> • athletes who don't work hard will regret it later

a) Write down **three** key topics you would expect the coach to cover in a speech given to the students at the event.

b) Write down your **three** key topics on a piece of paper as headings. Then write down **two** points the coach could make under each heading.

Q5 Read the following extract from a newspaper article.

> ### Kill Your Speed
>
> Speed limits must be reduced in urban areas. The current risk to lives from traffic is too great. If a driver runs over a pedestrian when he is doing 20 mph, there is a one in five chance he will kill them. This is already a high risk — so why are city speed limits usually as high as 30 mph? Being in a hurry is no excuse. Neither are the improvements in traffic control and pedestrian crossings.

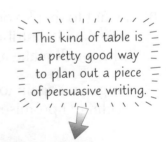

This kind of table is a pretty good way to plan out a piece of persuasive writing.

a) Imagine you're going to write a letter to the newspaper in reply to the article, either for or against the reduction of city speed limits. Draw a table with two columns, one for arguments which support your view, and one for points that are against it. From the extract, find **two** points to go under each heading.

b) Write down **two** more points, of your own, under each of the main headings.

c) Number the points you have under each heading in order of importance. Cross out any which seem unimportant.

Middle bit — keeps your nose away from your feet...

The middle bit of an essay may not have the emotional impact of the introduction or the incredible power of the conclusion. But, like the meat in a sandwich, it's still dead important.

Structuring Your Writing — Conclusions

Phew... on to the conclusion already. The conclusion is the last paragraph of an essay. It should bring everything together and tie it up nicely — in a triple reef knot perhaps.

Q1   Is the following statement true or false? Explain your answer.

"The conclusion is a good place to bring in new information. There is no need to be consistent with what has gone before in the essay — capturing the reader's interest is key."

Q2   Which **three** of the following things (**i-viii**) should you include in a conclusion?

i)   a final statement about the topic

ii)   a small portrait of Alan Rickman in charcoal

iii)   a summary of the main points in your essay

iv)   all the points in your essay explained in detail

v)   an introduction to a new topic

vi)   a rant about what you think

vii)   yesterday's mashed potatoes

viii) your own view on the topic

Q3   Match up each type of text (**i-iii**) to the right conclusion (**A, B, C**).

i)   a letter   **ii)**   a story   **iii)**   a persuasive text

A)   The band left the stage to deafening cheers. They grinned at each other, too dazed with happiness to speak. Their gig had been a triumph. At last, all their struggles had paid off. It was the best night of their lives.

B)   I want to thank you again for your kind donation. The money raised will contribute towards building a new school in Bolivia, which will make a huge difference to the local community.

C)   I urge you again to go home, dig out your bike from the back of the garage, and get cycling. I promise it will be the best decision you have ever made in your life.

Q4   Conclusions to persuasive texts can be tricky — you have to be forceful without being rude. Explain why each of these conclusions is good or bad.

a)   In conclusion, destroying the rainforest is probably not a great idea. It's pretty important and we might regret it if we cut it down. It would be nice if we campaigned a bit to try and save it.

b)   The rainforest is a unique and priceless resource. It provides us with oxygen and medicines, and is home to countless species of wildlife. We urgently need to stop its destruction in order to save it for future generations. Please, join the fight to protect our rainforest — once it is lost, it will be lost forever.

I wholeheartedly agree.

c)   I strongly believe that the rainforests shouldn't be cut down. Any other views are deeply misguided. It shows a real lack of intelligence that people could destroy something so precious. We should all campaign to stop the destruction of the rainforests. Anyone who doesn't is lazy or selfish.

Structuring Your Writing — Conclusions

You're nearly at the end of these questions on endings...

Q5 Copy out the correct statement from the choices below.

The ending of a story should:

i) leave the reader wondering what on earth happened.

ii) tie up all the loose ends in a satisfying way.

iii) bring in a flurry of new characters and ideas, to make it exciting.

Q6 The main points made in a persuasive essay are shown by the bullet points below. Write a conclusion for the essay based on these bullet points.

> ## Should testing on animals be allowed?
>
> **Main points made in essay:**
>
> * I believe that any unnecessary testing on animals should be banned.
> * Testing on animals is very cruel. Research shows that animals feel pain just like humans.
> * Animals are often bred purely to be tested on. They are not given the chance to experience any freedom in their life at all.
> * Make-up is still sometimes tested on animals, which seems unnecessary as this could be tested on humans instead.
> * Some people argue that testing on animals is necessary in order to develop new medicines to cure diseases that cause many people to suffer. However, I believe that testing on animals should be kept to a minimum to stop animals suffering.

Q7 Here's a summary of the middle section of the story. Write an ending paragraph for the story.

> ### What happens next...
>
> * Detective Anderson reads the ransom note left at the scene of the crime. "A million quid or you'll never see Chewy the Chihuahua again."
> * Chewy's owner, actress Philomena Fox, is in floods of tears. She tells Detective Anderson that the culprit is probably her ex-boyfriend, singer Silvester Smooth.
> * The detective heads to the recording studio where he finds Silvester's limo. There's a high-pitched whining coming from inside the car. It must be Chewy...

The end of the essay is nigh...

Don't go thinking "and they all lived happily ever after..." is going to do it — that's just lazy. Conclusions are the big finale, the last hurrah of your piece. Write a conclusion, and write it good.

Paragraphs

Putting your writing in proper paragraphs will give it a clear structure, and give the reader a clear idea of when you're making a new point.

Q1 1-5 below are the reasons for starting a new paragraph.
Match them with the paragraph changes in the bits of writing labelled A-E.

1. new point / topic   2. new person   3. different person speaks

4. new time being described   5. new place being described

A The Red Scare of 1919 was a time of paranoia in America about left-wing radicals. The Sacco and Vanzetti trial is a famous example.

The McCarthy communist witchhunts were a similar phenomenon. McCarthy was convinced that the US government was full of communists.

B Algeria was colonised in 1830 and remained under French rule until the revolution of the 1950s. The revolution was very violent and lasted from 1954 to 1962.

Egypt was different. It was never fully colonised, but was under a British protectorate from 1881.

C John walked over to the ostrich and raised his hat.

"How do you do sir?" he asked politely. However, the ostrich did not reply.

D Kirsty felt really angry about the play. She kicked the chair of the old lady sitting in front of her.

The old lady turned round and grinned a terrible grin. Slowly, she raised her stick.

Trapped! Hope I can get out of here by Christmas...

E Ernest Hemingway used to live in Key West in Florida. His favourite bar was called Sloppy Joe's.

If you go to Sloppy Joe's now it's in a different building and is a bit of a tourist trap.

Q2 A good paragraph sticks to one topic. Work out which sentences in the following paragraph are rambling off the main topic. Then write out a corrected version.

Pompeii was a small city of no great importance in the Roman world. Seneca does mention the town of Ostia in two of his letters. One of the few mentions Pompeii gets in ancient texts is in relation to a fight which broke out at the amphitheatre in which several people were killed. We can glean more information from the archaeological excavations at the site. From the size of the site it is estimated that it had about twenty thousand inhabitants. Pliny didn't live there, although he was killed by inhaling ash from the eruption. Evidence from the site includes: buildings, the contents of people's houses, wall paintings, graffiti and plaster casts of people who died in the eruption.

Q3 Copy out this extract from a short story, starting new paragraphs where needed.

As Myrna sat down at the kitchen table, she already felt full. So far she had eaten five blueberry tarts, ten Easter eggs, a rhubarb crumble and 76 fun-size chocolate bars. Ali ran into the room and saw the last piece of evidence, the double-cream layered pavlova still there on the kitchen table. "Come on, he's almost here!" he yelled. "I'm trying," groaned Myrna. Meanwhile, the dastardly Mr Smiker was walking slowly across the fields, his nose twitching in the breeze. The unmistakable scent of a missing double-cream layered pavlova filled his monstrous nostrils. He smiled a terrifying smile. Even his teeth were evil.

Paragraphs

Sadly, even your most impressive writing will read badly unless it's in proper paragraphs. Here's a couple more questions to get your paragraph skills shipshape and shiny.

Q4 Read the passage below, then fill in the table to show how each paragraph begins and what it is talking about. Use the phrases from the grey box to help you.

Most families argue about what to watch on the telly. The solution to this problem is a) to persuade your mum to buy everyone their own TV set, b) to watch something that no one really wants to see, just to be fair, or c) to encourage your brothers and sisters to go round to their friends' houses as often as possible (or, better still, to go and live there).

If you have satellite, the problem is even worse. How does anyone have time to read the telly guide for all those channels, never mind actually watch all the programmes?

An alternative to arguing about programmes is to turn off the TV. Instead, you could play a game such as chess or charades. At the same time, you could talk about your day at school. Then you could go and finish your homework, start your maths assignment, or read a book.

To be even more radical, you could choose not to have a TV. However, the problem with the no-telly approach is that you'll get regular visits from the TV detector people. They won't believe that you don't have a telly in the house and will want to know why you don't have a licence.

Paragraph	Begins	Talks about
1		
2		
3		
4		

To be even more radical…	alternative solution — don't watch TV
If you have satellite…	more radical solution — don't have TV
Most families argue…	further problem — satellite TV
An alternative to arguing…	basic problem and some solutions

Q5 If you're describing an event you should usually write things down in the order they happened. Put these sentences in order and write them out as a paragraph.

i) Hilary had been annoyed — she'd wanted to have an adventure, not to go home.

ii) Once, when Hilary was at primary school, she'd climbed over the playing field fence.

iii) Hilary had refused to be scared and had started walking as far from school as possible.

iv) After about two hours she had reached her own house.

v) All her friends had run away because they were scared.

Paragraphs

I love paragraphs. I'd write this top bit in paragraphs if I had enough space. Alas.

Q6   Here's a paragraph from a persuasive essay. Rearrange the sentences into the following order: 1) main point, 2) development of main point, 3) evidence (quotes and statistics).

> Seventy-five students make use of the bus service; that's a lot of extra cars. If our school bus was discontinued each child would have to travel to school individually. As the headteacher has said, "The pollution caused by the extra cars travelling to the school would have a bad effect on the environment." We all know that school buses are environmentally friendly.

Q7   These paragraphs only contain two sentences each.
Match the halves, and write them out.

a)   Rosie couldn't help but be grateful that the weekend had come at last.

b)   "Excuse me, can you tell me where the maternity ward is, please?" Grace asked politely.

c)   Beth approached the talent contest like a gladiator ready for battle.

i)   The hospital receptionist gave her a disapproving look, followed by a reluctant reply.

ii)   Joy rose up inside of her as she thought of going to visit her Dad on Sunday.

iii)   She waited confidently in the wings, staring down her fellow performers with an icy look.

Q8   Read the following paragraphs. Write a first sentence for each paragraph which introduces the main point it is making.

a)   In my view, unhealthy treats and snacks should be rejected in favour of healthier alternatives. It is important to follow a strict diet, and to avoid 'bad' foods, such as those containing too much fat, salt and artificial sugars.

b)   In my view, you can have a healthy diet and still enjoy some 'unhealthy' foods. As long as you don't eat too much of anything, the occasional 'unhealthy' dessert or bar of chocolate, for example, is nothing to be worried about.

Q9   The sentences in the paragraph below are mixed up.

Don't forget that a hard floor is much noisier and colder than a carpet. Of course, you can have the best of both worlds by using rugs on top of a hard surface. Do you need something that is easily cleaned (a hard floor), or something that is warm and comfortable (a soft carpet)? When choosing a new floor covering, consider the following points:

a)   Write out the sentence which should come first.

b)   Write down the phrases that gave you a clue to your answer for **a)**.

c)   Write out the rest of the paragraph in a sensible order.

Linking Paragraphs

OK, now your paragraph writing should be so polished, you could eat your dinner off it.
You've still got to make sure your paragraphs flow — i.e. follow on nicely from each other.

Q1   Write out the words or phrases below that are useful for linking paragraphs together.

i)   furthermore

ii)   another point of view is

iii) with hindsight

iv)   sociable types

v)   too right

vi)   a contrasting view is

vii) milking it

viii) however

ix)   another example of

x)   in addition to this

xi)   beyond comprehension

xii) on the other hand

Q2   A new paragraph should use a linking word or phrase to join it to the paragraph before.
Read these paragraphs and write an opening sentence for the paragraph that follows.

e.g. Cary Grant was a famous actor, at his peak in the 1940s and 1950s. Originally he was from Bristol, and his real name was Archibald Leach.

[The **next paragraph** is about Ingrid Bergman, a movie star in the 1940s and 1950s.]

Another movie star from the 1940s and 1950s was the actress Ingrid Bergman.

A Many years ago white lead was used in face powder. This resulted in women suffering from lead poisoning, although they didn't know what the cause of the illness was.

[The **next paragraph** is about how nowadays people know white lead is dangerous and don't use it for make-up.]

B The opinion of the school's board of governors about truancy is fairly harsh. They suggest that pupils should be punished with detentions, and that the parents of repeat offenders should be sent warning letters and fines.

[The **next paragraph** is about the opinion of the Parents' Association, which is less harsh.]

C Many young children enjoy cartoons. They are bright and appealing to look at and feature easily recognisable characters. A lot of imagination and humour is put into popular cartoons, and this attracts children's interest.

[The **next paragraph** is about how many parents disapprove of cartoons because they think they are mindless drivel.]

Q3   Write two paragraphs. In the first one describe the village, town or city where you lived when you were ten. In the second paragraph describe the primary school you went to there. Link the two paragraphs together smoothly.

Q4   Write two paragraphs: the first describing your views about fashion, the second describing your parents' views about fashion. Link the two paragraphs together smoothly.

Basic Punctuation and Speech Marks

"A page on speech and question marks? Oh, and exclamation marks. No problem!"

Q1   Decide whether each of the following sentences needs to include speech marks.
Copy out the ones which do, adding speech marks in the right places.

a)   Holly calmly told the policeman that the prize-winning parrots would never
have escaped if Kate hadn't forced her to come to the zoo in the first place.

b)   Anyway, parrots are boring, I was nowhere near them, she said.

c)   PC Redman warned that unless Holly started co-operating
soon, there were going to be serious consequences.

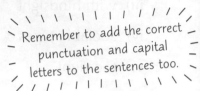
Remember to add the correct punctuation and capital letters to the sentences too.

d)   As they started leading her towards the police van,
Holly panicked and shouted it was Kate!

e)   PC Redman was starting to ask himself why he'd joined the police force when he
spotted some brightly coloured feathers moving towards the hot dog stand.

Q2   Copy out the following passage, putting in **two** question marks and **three** exclamation
marks in the appropriate places. You may need to make the odd letter a capital too.

> Jake burst through the door of the garage shop.
> "Freeze" he shouted. He was scared; he could feel the sweat rolling
> down his forehead and flooding his eyes. He moved towards the cashier,
> holding the bag out in one hand, grasping his water pistol in the other.
> "Oh my life" said the cashier, "Jake Smithson, what are you doing"
> Jake stopped in his tracks. He had been told that a pair of tights over
> the head would render any human being unrecognisable.
> "I'm not Jake Smithson," he said, backing away.
> "Yes you are, I used to serve you lunch at St Hilda's Primary School.
> Fancy that what are you getting up to these days" she said. Quietly,
> she pressed the police alarm under the counter.

Q3   Copy out the following sentences, adding correct punctuation (including speech marks).

a)   I'm going home said Slim I've had enough.

b)   My name is Otto said the stranger and I will have my revenge on you all.

c)   I think I'm coming down with the flu said Anar. Oh, I am sorry said Mark.
So am I said Anar.

d)   She was wearing an awful red shirt said Lena. But I think she thought she
looked fabulous said Charlotte.

e)   You must pay me a million pounds shouted the robber.

f)   Now then, young man said the policeman. What is it officer I replied.

Sentences, Phrases and Clauses

There's no way around it, I'm afraid — you have to learn to use language correctly.

Q1 Read parts **a)-i)**. Write down why each one isn't a proper sentence.

a) The dog walked slowly up the drive, regretting the mess he'd made of the roses

b) the wind in my hair.

c) Paul said that he liked Vienna

d) The Romans' legendary cruelty to Octavia.

e) Giauri and the dog.

f) she wants to go but her father thinks it's a silly idea

g) Before the winter.

h) We went to the seaside

i) Bananas for £2.20 a kilo.

Psst — you ain't seen me, right?

Q2 Write down whether **a)-i)** are phrases or clauses.

a) the hedgehog's evil spikes

b) in the fish tank

c) we went to Harini's house

d) up to the river

e) on the way to the bus

f) Rita is gorgeous

g) in the autumn

h) Omar paused thoughtfully

i) despite the heavy rain

Q3 Match up the most appropriate phrases and the clauses below (you can only use each one once). Write them out as sentences, putting a comma between the phrase and the clause.

Phrases	Clauses
a) Before the start of term	**1)** you can see fish swimming.
b) In the Atlantic Ocean	**2)** you can't make mustard sauce.
c) In the new school play	**3)** my brother has a new bedroom.
d) Without a bit of mustard	**4)** dinosaurs are now extinct.
e) Without a doubt	**5)** my teacher explained it all again.
f) Textbook in hand	**6)** the acting is impressive.
g) During her latest tantrum	**7)** Kim threw an egg against the wall.
h) Up in the attic	**8)** I'll have to cram in lots of fun.

Commas, Semicolons and Colons

Commas, semicolons and colons are all used to break sentences up into manageable chunks. Try pausing slightly where you want to put the punctuation to see if it sounds right.

Q1 Copy out the following sentences, adding commas to make the meaning clearer.

a) Walking beside the miniature poodle Harley felt very tall indeed.

b) I asked her about her holiday but she ignored me.

c) Scurrying out of the way of the headmistress Dana looked a bit sheepish.

d) As soon as he saw Frank the baboon became angry.

Q2 Copy out the following sentences, adding two commas to each to make the meaning clearer.

a) The Lake District which is in northern England is a popular holiday destination.

b) Not long afterwards with her hair in a complete mess my sister returned to the ranch.

c) The weather was far too hot for Bernard a large bull terrier as he ran across the park.

d) Stephen who works with my brother likes to play golf on the weekend.

Q3 All these sentences have colons missing.
Copy out the sentences, adding colons in the right place.

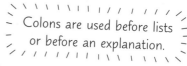
Colons are used before lists or before an explanation.

a) I'll tell you how I did it I walked up to him and asked.

b) All I want from my hamster is companionship, devotion and a number one single.

c) The show was a disaster no one remembered their lines and the set collapsed.

d) You should bring the following things an inflatable dinghy, a life jacket and a foghorn.

e) Tariq was giving up on being a secret agent he couldn't stop telling everyone about it.

Q4 The following sentences have semicolons in the wrong place.
Copy out the sentences, putting semicolons in the correct places.

a) The star required: a trailer; with a jacuzzi, preferably at maximum temperature three servants, including a manicurist; a separate dog kennel, which had; to be red and salmon sandwiches without crusts.

Semicolons are used to break up clauses in a sentence, or to break up lists when the items have additional punctuation.

b) The footballer had it all: a strong; left foot a good, well-trained eye; for the ball lightning; pace and nerves of steel.

c) He walked; into the room it was completely dark.

d) Jim had made lots of money he owned; a large percentage of Birmingham.

Apostrophes

Teachers love complaining that 'young people these days' don't know how to use apostrophes. Do this page and you'll be able to knock them sideways with your apostrophe know-how.

Q1 Read the following sentences a)-f). Copy down the sentences where <u>it's</u> and <u>its</u> are wrong and change them so they're right.

a) Its important to drink lots of water throughout the day.

b) Why do I always have to wash up? It's not fair that Leo never does it.

c) Its sunny outside — why stay indoors?

d) The driver wanted the car repaired because its' gearbox was making funny noises.

e) Charlie loved his new room, with its pink wallpaper and purple carpet.

f) It's hardly surprising that no children like Peter: all their parents do.

Q2 Apostrophes are used to show that something belongs to something else. Copy out the sentences below, putting apostrophes in the right places.

    e.g.   Sentence: Philippas cows are a bit special.
              Correction: **Philippa's cows are a bit special.**

a) The ostriches beaks were all shiny.

b) My brother Alex has got Dads old car.

c) She gave him her mums favourite handkerchief, realising too late that it was covered in snot.

d) The childrens section of the menu was uninspiring.

e) Matts piano was six feet tall; he couldn't reach the pedals.

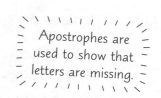

Honestly, she's just shy because you're here.

Q3 In informal writing, it's common to combine, or shorten, certain words. Copy the sentences below, combining or shortening the highlighted words.

a) I **do not** want to trouble you, but your Alsatian is in my garage.

b) The boxer **will not** fight without his lucky rabbit's foot.

c) **Do** you **not** think it's strange how celebrities get thinner every year?

d) **It is** the best piece of music I have ever heard.

e) It **is not** that unusual for people to have two part-time jobs.

f) I **cannot** go to the gym. I **will not** go to the gym. I **do not** want to go to the gym.

Apostrophes are used to show that letters are missing.

FYI — Philippa's cows can dance like Anton du Beke...

It was like a really bad cheese advert — they looked all cow-like, but then suddenly they were off, foxtrotting across the field. [Well, you think of something interesting to say about apostrophes.]

Use Different Words

This is a great section because there are lots of great questions about great tricks that will make your writing really great. Bored? Avoid this mess by using different words in your writing.

Q1 The following passages use the same words again and again.
Copy out the passages, and replace the repeated words with more interesting synonyms.

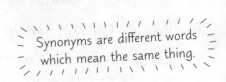

Synonyms are different words which mean the same thing.

a) The film I saw this weekend was really good. The acting was really good which was good because the characters were quite difficult to get right. I was hoping it would be good because it's based on a really good book — one of my favourites, actually. It's a good example of a book that both adults and teenagers can enjoy reading.

b) The most horrible food in the world has to be baked beans. The sauce they come in is horrible, and the beans taste horrible too. One of my friends eats baked bean salad, a horrible mixture of cold baked beans and lettuce leaves — it's just horrible.

c) It's a bit embarrassing but I find frogs really scary. I don't like the way their scary eyes stare at you when you walk past them. But the most scary thing about frogs is probably the noise they make — it scares me. There's a film coming out next year called 'March of the Frogs', but I think I'll be too scared to go and see it.

Q2 Write down a more interesting verb instead of 'went' in each sentence.

a) Hayley **went** to the museum in her new car.

b) Mahmoud **went** to the box office, hoping he'd be in time to get a ticket.

c) Despite all the fuss she had made, Janice **went** in the aeroplane in the end.

d) Becky **went** around the shops after her gran, wishing she wasn't there.

e) The lamb **went** along the grass, looking very cute.

Come on, Janice, it'll be fine.

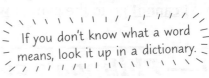

Q3 Replace the simple words with the most appropriate complex ones from the box.

a) "I don't know about you, William, but I think throwing cold porridge at Mr Wimpington is very **rude**."

b) Everyone **liked** Rowan — he was welcoming, loyal and kind.

c) Aron was in trouble for spreading **nasty** rumours about people.

retrieved   insisted
disrespectful
malicious   admired

d) Finally, after what seemed like a decade spent looking under her bed, Jen **took out** her ski outfit.

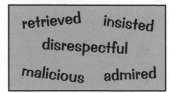

If you don't know what a word means, look it up in a dictionary.

e) "It was Emily who did it first!" Assallah **said**.

Don't Be Boring

To make your writing more interesting you can: vary the length of your sentences (i.e. some short, some long), vary how you start your sentences, and avoid using too many clichés.

Q1 Copy out each of these sentences, splitting each one into two shorter sentences. You may need to remove a few words for the new sentence to make sense.

a) Isabel had only got one ticket and she didn't want to give it away.

b) Pancakes with sugar and lemon are good but jam filling is also nice.

c) Daria flew over the wall and landed in a heap at the bottom of the ditch.

d) St Malo is really hot in the summer so you can go swimming in the sea.

e) Una was going to miss the plane unless she could grab a lift on the boy's skateboard.

Q2 The following paragraph is poorly written. Improve it by making some sentences shorter, and others longer — do it by splitting or combining sentences. You may need to add or remove a few words.

> Rita Hayworth was born in 1918. She was born in America. Her original name was Margarita Cansino. Her father was Spanish. From a young age she danced in a stage act with her father. She spent a lot of time practising her dancing. This meant she missed out on most of her education. In the late 1930s, she started to get small roles in films, but the American film industry didn't like the fact that she looked Spanish so her appearance was changed in the following ways: her black hair was dyed red, and her hairline was made higher by electrolysis; in addition to this her Spanish-sounding name was changed to Rita Hayworth.

Q3 Rewrite these paragraphs so that the sentences don't all start with the same word.

a) She was sitting on a bench in the park. She saw a duck coming towards her. She reached into her bag for some bread. She bent down to feed it to him. She spotted her friend walking towards her from across the grass.

b) I love rabbits. I have three rabbits called Eugene, Raymond and Nigel. I play fetch with them sometimes. I like Nigel best because he can play the piano.

Q4 Rewrite this paragraph, replacing the highlighted clichés with more interesting language.

> Then, just when I thought <u>the ball was in my court</u>, <u>who should walk in</u> but my old nemesis, Miss Rumple! That was a <u>shock to the system</u>. I had <u>no room for manoeuvre</u>; I had to <u>take the bull by the horns</u>. I took the catapult from my pocket, saying to myself, "<u>It's not over until the fat lady sings.</u>"

Adjectives

Using adjectives makes your descriptive writing much better. Suddenly, it isn't just a piece of writing. It's an elegantly crafted, carefully selected, stylishly-worded piece of writing.

Q1   Underline all the adjectives in the following passage.

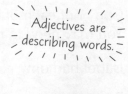

Adjectives are describing words.

> A glorious day had begun. The powder-blue sky was dotted with cotton-wool clouds. A swallow flitted through the still air, her sharp wings slicing a path effortlessly. Her turns were swift and precise; she was supreme. Below her, on the tiny country lanes, red-faced humans crawled along in their metal coffins, sweating and sighing their way to the crowded beaches.

Q2   Copy out the piece above, changing the adjectives to show that the swallow is small and that the humans are powerful. You may have to change some other words too.

Q3   Identify the nouns in the following sentences.
Then copy out the sentences, adding an adjective to all of the nouns.

A noun is a thing (e.g. a person, place or object).

> **e.g.**   The ⟨man⟩ was happy because he'd bought a ⟨painting⟩
> *The <u>rich</u> man was happy because he'd bought a <u>beautiful</u> painting.*

a)   The boy was scared that the dog would attack him.

b)   The mouse began to creep towards the dinosaur.

c)   Finally, the woman slumped down into her armchair.

d)   A wave came towards the shore and drenched the sunbathers.

e)   In the park near my house there is an oak tree.

f)   I didn't know until that moment how I would cope in such a situation.

g)   It was three days before they realised that the hamster had escaped.

h)   "It is a fact that Robert Mitchum was an actor," said my mum.

Q4   Copy out these sentences and fill in the blanks with adjectives.

a)   Animal testing is .... and ....

b)   School uniform is ...., ... and ....

c)   Football is definitely the most .... sport in the world.

d)   Mr Beak's nose was incredibly ....

e)   The film was absolutely ...., particularly the opening scenes.

Comparing

Comparisons help your reader to build a picture of what you're describing. Make sure your comparisons are sensible — saying your gerbil is as cute as a paperclip is no use to anyone.

Q1 Copy and complete the sentences below, adding a word to each to complete the comparison.

The posh word for this sort of comparison is 'simile'.

a) Ilona turned to the headteacher furiously, and screamed like a ....

b) As he crept over to the side of the ship, Levi's shoes squeaked like ....

c) Her face was as red as a ....

d) The chips looked gorgeous. Henry was as hungry as a ....

There's more than one possible answer.

e) The bell rang. Students rushed out into the corridors like a ....

Q2 For each of the sentences a)-e), choose the most sensible word from the box to complete the comparison.

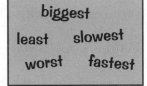

biggest
least   slowest
worst   fastest

a) It wasn't surprising that Louis won the race. He was the .... runner in the school.

b) Entering the lion enclosure dressed as a giant steak was the .... idea that Zayn had come up with so far.

c) "Come on!" shouted Niall. "This is the .... moving traffic I've ever been in!"

d) Selfish as always, Liam took the .... slice of pie for himself.

e) Everyone knew that Harry, who had a lifelong fear of water, was probably the .... likely to complete the sponsored swim.

Q3 Write out and correct the comparisons below.

There's more than one way to correct some of them.

a) Clare's picture is more beautifuler than Jessica's.

b) Petar is more sportier than Ian.

c) "Oh, Imogen," said Jane, "that is the most bestest cake I've ever tasted."

d) Matthew had always been jealous of Luke because he was more better at wrestling.

e) Polina reckoned she was the most cleverest member of the family.

Take a look at the next section — it's even better...

There are lots of different types of comparisons you can use, so mix them up a bit to keep your writing interesting — just remember not to use more than one at a time, and to make them sensible.

Practice Questions

These practice questions give you the chance to stretch your mental legs a little. You need to think carefully about what you're going to write — and try to bring together all the things you've practised in sections 6-9. Don't worry if that seems like a lot to handle — there's three whole pages of help on how to answer the first question.

PRACTICE QUESTION 1: HOMEWORK

This is an extract from the 'Learning in Britain' website, written by teacher Edna Monich:

> We need to open up a discussion about how much homework pupils are given. Some of my Year 9 students have up to two hours of homework each evening. This makes them feel stressed and tired, and stops them from taking part in extracurricular activities. Homework may allow children to practise skills and learn information, but that is no excuse to give them excessive amounts of work.

Write an article for your school magazine about homework. Argue either that homework is useful, or that pupils should be given less homework.

Q1 You need to work out your audience first.

a) Who is your article supposed to be aimed at? Choose from options **i)-iv)**.

    i) teachers in the North West

    ii) a mixture of teachers, pupils and parents

    iii) the readers of the 'Learning in Britain' website

    iv) Edna Monich

b) Write down the part of the question which lets you know who will read your article.

Q2 The purpose of your article is very important.

a) What is the purpose of the article? Choose from options **i)-iii)**.

    i) to inform   **ii)** to argue   **iii)** to entertain

b) Write a sentence explaining what this purpose means in your own words.

Q3 You also need to think about the style of your article.

a) Write out the words below which you think describe the style appropriate for the article.

> formal   angry   sarcastic   posh
>
> apologetic   polite   informal   aggressive

b) Explain why you picked those words.

Practice Questions

Now that you've worked out a few basics about the text you need to write, here's a page to help you plan your answer. Copy it out nice and big and then answer the questions below.

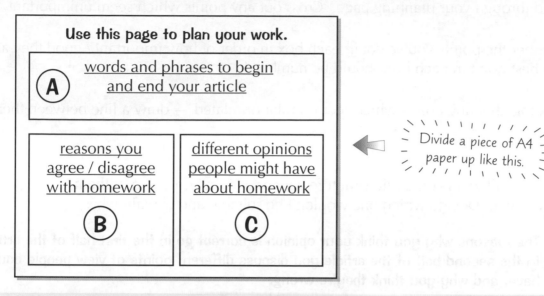

Use this page to plan your work.

(A) words and phrases to begin and end your article

(B) reasons you agree / disagree with homework

(C) different opinions people might have about homework

Divide a piece of A4 paper up like this.

Q4 a) Which of the following sets of words and phrases do you think would be most appropriate to <u>begin</u> your article? Choose one set or words and phrases from options **i)-iv)**.

   i) good evening / I welcome you on behalf of my school / today I would like to talk about

   ii) homework is an important issue / I believe that / should pupils be given less homework?

   iii) hiya / people who don't agree are idiots / my mum says this as well

   iv) there's no right answer to this really / I might be wrong, I'm not sure / I'll give it a go

b) Give a reason for your choice, and explain why each of the other options is wrong.

c) Now fill in box A on your planning page, using your answer to part **a)**.

Q5 Decide whether you are going to argue for or against homework.

a) Read the question again, and find two points in Edna's article which support your view. Write them into box B on your planning page.

b) Think of two more reasons why your opinion is right, and write them into the same box.

Q6 You need to think about why people might disagree with your opinion.

a) Read the question again and find two points in Edna's article which disagree with your opinion. Write them into box C on your planning page.

b) Think of two more reasons why other people might not agree with your opinion and write them into the same box.

82

Practice Questions

It's not over yet. More questions about that question planning page coming right up...

Q7 **a)** Read through your planning page. Cross out any points which seem unimportant.

b) Number the points you've got in each box in order of how important / good they are. The best point in each box should be number 1.

c) Link together any points which seem similar or related — draw a line between them.

Q8 i)-iii) are all ways you could structure your article, but only two of them are correct. Decide which one wouldn't be suitable and explain why.

i) The reasons why you think your opinion is correct go in the first half of the article. In the second half of the article you discuss different points of view people could have, and why you think they're wrong.

ii) Each paragraph of your article compares a point for, and a point against homework. You argue that the points which agree with your opinion are better.

iii) Each paragraph of your article gives a reason why your point of view is correct, and backs it up with examples and evidence. This means you don't have to discuss other points of view.

Q9 Write a full answer to the question on p.80. It should cover 1-2 sides of A4. Use your planning page to help you.

Q10 When you're finished, read through your answer and check the following things:

☐ The article has a clear introduction and conclusion.
☐ The article is convincing. It gives good reasons to support one point of view. It acknowledges other points of view exist, and gives reasons why they are wrong.
☐ The structure of the article is signposted for the reader.
☐ The article is written in paragraphs.
☐ Interesting vocabulary and sentence structures are used.
☐ A range of punctuation is used correctly, e.g. commas, colons, semicolons.
☐ The spelling is good.

Q11 Make any corrections to your answer neatly.

Practice Questions

Here's another practice question for you to have a crack at. It's a great chance for you to put everything you've learnt into action. Don't worry — it still comes with some planning hints.

PRACTICE QUESTION 2: A CASE OF MISTAKEN IDENTITY

Your local newspaper is running a story-writing competition for young people.

> Young Writers' Story Competition
> The theme of this year's competition is mistaken identity.
> Write an imaginative story on this topic. You should write about:
> * The characters who are mistaken for each other, and why they're so alike
> * Who mixes them up
> * The result of the mix-up
> The winning entry will be published in the Herald newspaper.

Write your entry to the competition.

Q1   Sketch out a grid like this, and fill it in.

Question	Answer
What is the purpose of the piece of writing?	
Who is going to read it?	
Write down three words which describe the style of the piece of writing.	

Q2 a)   Write down three things that the question tells you should be included in your story.

b)   Use these three things you've learnt as a way to organise your planning. Write them out as headings on a piece of paper. Then spend 5 minutes thinking of ideas, and scribbling them down under the headings.

Q3   Write a full answer to the question. It should cover just over a side of A4. Use the plan you have written to help you.

Q4   When you have finished writing, spend a couple of minutes reading through your work and correcting any mistakes.

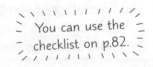
You can use the checklist on p.82.

The section's almost over — keep going, one more...

Don't be scared of writing longer pieces. Planning your answer is the key. If it helps, write down "audience, purpose, style, structure, paragraphs, interesting sentences" at the top of your plan.

Practice Questions

Here's three more practice questions to try. Don't forget to plan before you start writing.

PRACTICE QUESTION 3: TODAY'S NEWS

Write an article for a newspaper about an accident at a major sporting event. You should make your account believable, but you can make up the facts.

You should include:
- a headline
- a description of what happened
- quotes from people who witnessed the accident
- information about what action is going to be taken to improve safety in the future

Use this page to plan your work.

a headline for your article

what happened, when and where

quotes from witnesses

what's going to happen next

PRACTICE QUESTION 4: BULLYING IN SCHOOL

Your school is trying to tackle bullying.

> Calling All Students
> We would like you to produce a leaflet to advise students on how to deal with bullying. It should comment on the advantages and disadvantages of different actions students can take, e.g.
> - talking to a teacher
> - talking to a friend or parent
> - avoiding or ignoring the bullies
> - fighting or talking back to the bullies

Write the text for the leaflet.

Use this page to plan your work.

words and phrases to begin and end your discussion

different ways to deal with bullying

advantages and disadvantages of each suggestion

PRACTICE QUESTION 5: NO SHAKESPEARE AT LOCAL THEATRE

A local theatre has decided to stop putting on Shakespeare plays.
This is an extract from a letter by an English teacher to the local newspaper.

> The local theatre company has completely failed to see two important points:
> 1. Shakespeare's plays are not boring; they are filled with humour, suspense and drama.
> 2. Students in local schools studying the plays gain a lot from seeing them performed.

Write a letter to the managing director of the local theatre, Marcus Straw, arguing that Shakespeare's plays should still be performed there. You don't need to include an address.

A job, a job, my kingdom for a job!

Answers

Answers

Section One — Audience and Purpose

Page 1 — Audience

Q1 A — ii)
  B — iv)
  C — i)
  D — iii)

Q2 • Text A describes what happened in a fairly impersonal style, and it quotes a description of the event.
  • Text B uses simple language and explains a word ("algae") that the younger children might not understand.
  • Text C is written in an informal style and uses casual, chatty language as if writing to a friend, e.g. "Did I tell you" and "bigger than Gavin's bike".
  • Text D uses formal and respectful language, and acknowledges that the reader knows a lot about the subject.

Q3 **a)** adults
  b) toddlers
  c) school pupils

Page 2 — Purpose

Q1 **a)** A — iv)
    B — iii)
    C — ii)
    D — i)
  b) • Text A explains why something happened and gives reasons.
    • Text B uses clever techniques such as rhetorical questions, and groups of three adjectives, to try and get the reader to agree with the argument.
    • Text C builds suspense to entertain the reader, e.g. by using ellipses.
    • Text D includes facts and figures about the topic to improve the reader's understanding.

Q2 *Any reasonable answer, for example:*
  There are currently around 34 million hens in the UK that are laying eggs for **our benefit**. The demand for eggs has meant that 16 million of these **poor** hens are kept in small, **dark and cramped** cages. These cages are usually stacked on top of each other indoors, and are often shared between three or four birds — **can you imagine what it would be like to never see daylight?**
  Luckily, most of the remaining 18 million hens are 'free range'. These hens have continuous access to **vitally important** outdoor space which they can roam freely **and happily**. **We should all buy free range eggs,** even though they're more expensive than eggs from caged hens. **Many** studies have shown that there are higher quantities of nutrients in eggs from free range hens, **so happy hens means better eggs for all of us, too**.

Page 3 — Context

Q1 *Any reasonable answers, for example:*
  a) The purpose of marriage among the upper classes was to maintain or increase the social standing of the family.
  b) It was a woman's role to marry well, for the good of her family.

Q2 *Any reasonable answers, for example:*
  a) Men were very tired and ill-equipped: "Men marched asleep. Many had lost their boots".
  b) The author shows his disgust with the war by describing the terrible conditions that he and the other soldiers suffered. When he writes in the first person he shows how the war has upset him — he describes how he relives the awful things he has seen in his dreams.
  c) It suggests that war was seen as a glorious and noble thing in society at the time.

Section Two — Reading — The Basics

Page 4 — Finding the Important Bits

Q1

Description	Fact
Year PB Animation Studio was created	1998
Founded by...	Paul Black
Paul Black's current position	Managing Director
Total number of employees today	230

Q2 20 centimetres

Q3 wire frames (or armatures)

Q4 rod-and-joint structures

Q5 iii) 24

Q6 In order for the characters' movements to appear realistic.

Q7 The quality of its 3D animation.

Page 5 — Finding the Important Bits

Q8 **a)** Carrie darted round the corner into a dingy side-street full of discarded wooden crates.
  b) followed by Ben, who stopped and bent over, panting. He felt like he'd been out of breath ever since...

Answers

c) ever since they'd left the Pirate Academy.

d) the leering, cruel face of Captain Hack.

e) must walk the plank.

f) failing to hand in homework

g) Ben dashed forward with a yell, and managed to slip between Captain Hack's legs.

h) Ben ripped a thin plank of wood from a nearby crate

Q9 Suddenly they were aware of a shadow looming over them.

Q10 She's about to use it as a sword against Captain Hack. The part of the text is: "Then she remembered her sword-fighting lessons, and crouched with the plank in her hand, ready to defend herself against her pirate tutor."

Page 6 — Summarising

Q1 The King, Felix, the King's father, the King's courtier, Prime Minister Katan, two attendants (and the captured knights and the dragons for extra bonus points!).

Q2 The King and Felix

Q3 a) The King remembers when his father ruled, and knights were **easier** to control. **He starts to think about his childhood when he played with his toys in the garden.** Then he decides that something must be done about the knights.

b) ii) He seems angry with Felix, but is easily distracted by memories of his childhood.

Q4 The King accuses Felix of failing to stop the knights from escaping. He tells Prime Minister Katan to tie Felix up, take him to Vertis Ledge, and leave him to the dragons.

Q5 The King is angry because all of his captured knights have escaped. He reminisces about when his father was king and his own childhood. He blames Felix for allowing the knights to escape. He instructs the Prime Minister to tie Felix up and leave him to the dragons on Vertis Ledge. As Felix is taken away, he threatens the King.

Page 7 — Working Out What's Going On

Q1

Event	Order in extract
Looks for tickets	2
Puts milk bottles outside	5
Wakes up	1
Has an accident in the kitchen	3
Puts front door keys with tickets	4

Q2 without them she *definitely* wouldn't be going on holiday today.

Q3 before sacrificing two of the dishes to the floor in a flurry of ceramic and congealed Chinese takeaway.

Q4 ii) Mrs Hanrahan knocked over two dirty dishes, and they smashed on the floor.

Q5 The front door locks behind her.

Q6 *Any reasonable answer, for example:*
Mrs Hanrahan won't be able to get back into the house because the front door has locked and she left the keys inside. She won't be able to get the tickets, so she won't be able to go on holiday.

Page 8 — Point, Example, Explanation

Q1 Hanif strongly dislikes the rabbits and wants to get rid of them.

Q2 iii) Hanif wants to get rid of the rabbits. He calls them "stinking", which shows that he doesn't like them.

Q3 i) Hanif has a strong opinion about the rabbits.

Q4 Milla is nervous.

Q5 Milla glanced around the street nervously.

Q6 ii) Milla seems to be worried that someone will see her dumping the envelope in the bin.

Q7 Miles says that he'll be fine, but the fact that there is "a hint of a tear in his eye" shows that he's not feeling fine at all. He's actually feeling quite upset about something, but he's trying to hide it.

Answers

Answers

Page 9 — Different Types of Text

Q1 Epilepsy — The Facts — A
Using your T-300 — D
Waiting — B
A Man Alone — C

Q2 A and D

Q3 Poem — B
Story — C
Manual — D
Magazine article — A

Q4 a) fact
b) opinion
c) opinion
d) fact

Section Three — Reading — The Details

Page 10 — Choice of Vocabulary

Q1 technical language — a science textbook
formal language — a letter from the council
simple language — a story for a young child

Q2 *Any reasonable answer, for example:*
It uses slang to make the reader feel that the text is chatting to them.

Q3 *Any reasonable answer, for example:*
Slang makes the boy's speech sound more natural.

Q4 ii) Technical language shows that a writer knows a lot about a subject.

Page 11 — Similes and Metaphors

Q1 a) neither
b) simile
c) metaphor

Q2 ii) The shouting audience sounded noisy and tuneless, like wolf howls.

Q3 simile

Q4

Thing being described	Description the writer uses	Simile or Metaphor	What this means
Leo Ryder	he was a monster	metaphor	he was angry and impressive
Arnie X playing guitar	possessed by the ghost of Jimi Hendrix	metaphor	he played as well as Jimi Hendrix
Jay Bryson beating the drums	as if they were fires to be put out	simile	he looked frantic
	he managed to keep time as faithfully as an honest referee	simile	he kept time very well

Page 12 — Personification, Alliteration and Onomatopoeia

Q1 The willow tree — waved its boughs frantically.
The chest — waited patiently to be opened.
The moon — hid shyly behind the clouds.
The wind — wailed noisily.

Q2 *Any reasonable answers, for example:*
a) Slashing rain started the summer storm.
b) Cool, calm and collected, the cat crept through the casino.

Q3 *Any reasonable answers, for example:*
a) crash, bang, boom
b) screech, zoom, growl

Q4 a) Terrifying Twister Terrorises Town
b) whooshing
c) it was staring right back at me

Page 13 — Imagery

Q1 *Any reasonable answer, for example:*
"His heart hammered like a drum in his chest."
This shows that Inspector Graham was nervous because his heart was beating fast.

Q2 a) The room was an icy tomb.
b) *Any reasonable answer, for example:*
It makes the reader feel cold and tense.

Q3 crouching as if about to pounce at the Inspector.

Q4 iii) The stone carving is described as if it is alive — this effect is called personification.

Q5 The river flowed gently past the houses as if it didn't want to wake up the slumbering inhabitants.

Page 14 — Mood

Q1 A — tense
B — sad
C — happy

Q2 No. She watches her friends open their envelopes first, and then opens hers very slowly: "Her fingers tugged gently at the envelope".

Q3 The word "weep" makes it sound as if the ceilings are crying and upset, just like the family after the dog died.

Q4 It shows that Daniel is happy, because it makes him sound like an animal without any worries.

Q5 i) They slow the pace down before Rachel opens the envelope, which builds up suspense.

Q6 B — the description of sadness hanging heavily in the house gives the feeling of unhappiness. This fits the mood of B.

Answers

Q7 It shows that the family are sad about the dog — they don't speak very much or make eye contact. The phrase makes the whole text seem very sad.

Page 15 — Layout

Q1 A diary or journal — each entry is dated, with shortened forms of days and months.

Q2 To show when things happened, and to point out the start of each entry.

Q3 ii) To make the article feel like a conversation between the writer and the reader.

Q4 To make the text easier to follow, and to make it easy to refer back to points quickly.

Q5 They provide extra tips and explanations of the information in the list.

Q6 They link each tip to the correct numbered point.

Page 16 — Structure

Q1 It draws the reader in because it points out that the reader won't have heard of Andrew Bright, but soon he will be very famous.

Q2 The writer explains what happens in 'A Tale of Two Celebrities'.

Q3 The first paragraph introduces Andrew Bright, and the second paragraph tells you what the review is about. After reading the first paragraph, the reader will want to know what Andrew Bright has done that will make him famous.

Q4 The third paragraph explains why some people will like the book, and why it will be a big seller, but the fourth paragraph explains why some people won't like the book.

Q5 To contrast the two different opinions that people will have about the book.

Q6 i) The last sentence refers back to the introduction and sums up the main point of the review.

Q7 Use your answers to questions 1, 3, 5 and 6 to write your answer to this question.

Page 17 — Stories

Q1 a) third person
b) first person
c) first person
d) third person

Q2 ii) Sam and Kelly go for a walk in the woods.
v) They get lost and night begins to fall.
iv) They decide to take shelter for the night in a hollow tree.
i) Huddled up in the tree, they hear scary noises in the woods.
vi) They realise that the noise is a rescue party that has come looking for them.
iii) The rescue party take them safely home and they fall asleep on the sofa.

Q3 Bravery.
Any reasonable explanation, for example:
It is about a character who chooses to go to war in someone else's place. That is a brave thing to do.

Q4 ii) It shows that she is determined to join the army in place of her father.

Page 18 — Poetry

Q1 a) Wrapped up in a five-pound note.
b) Where civil blood makes civil hands unclean.
c) And found that he only had two.
d) In the forests of the night,
e) Glorious, the sun.

Q2 limerick — Q1 c)
sonnet — Q1 b)
haiku — Q1 e)
regular rhyming pattern — Q1 a) (and Q1 b))
rhyming couplets — Q1 d)

Q3 A verse is the same thing as a **stanza**. Each verse is made up of a group of **lines**. Verses in a poem have **different** words but they often follow the **same** pattern of syllables and **rhyming**.

Page 20 — Comparing Texts

Q1 *The Macaque Monkeys of Japan* — Diary
I, Monkey — Story
Monkey Behaviour — Magazine article

Q2 *Any reasonable answer, for example:*
• they're excited and buzzing around like annoying flies
• faces as pale as their white coats

Q3 *Any reasonable answer, for example:*
maybe have a chat about the weather

Q4 *Any reasonable answer, for example:*
It worked!

Answers

Q5 *Any reasonable answer, for example:*
- To make the text easier to follow
- To divide the text up into days because it is a diary

Q6 i) Macaque monkeys currently living in the centre of the island

Q7 ii) The monkey is more intelligent than the scientists realise. The monkey tells the story from his point of view, which shows the scientists are wrong.

Q8 i) The writer thinks that humans are not ruled by instinct, but that all animals and insects are.

Page 21 — Comparing Texts

Q9 ii) All three texts are about whether the behaviour of monkeys is purely instinctive.

Q10

Name of extract	The Macaque Monkeys of Japan	I, Monkey	Monkey Behaviour
Is the extract fiction or non-fiction?	non-fiction	fiction	non-fiction
Is the language formal or informal?	Informal	Informal	Formal
Is there a first-person narrator?	Yes	Yes	No
Does the writer use facts to back up their points?	Yes	No	Yes
Does the writer think that animals are ruled by instinct?	No	No	Yes

Q11 *Your answer could include the following points:*
- *The Macaque Monkeys of Japan* is broken up by the days that things are happening. This makes the text easy to follow, and it also shows where each new day begins.
- *I, Monkey* is laid out in long paragraphs.

Q12 *Your answer could include the following points:*
- *I, Monkey* uses informal language.
- *I, Monkey* uses humour.
- *Monkey Behaviour* uses formal language.
- There is no humour in *Monkey Behaviour*.

Q13 *Your answer could include the following points:*
- The writer of *The Macaque Monkeys of Japan* is trying to prove that the behaviour patterns of monkeys can change.
- By the end of the *The Macaque Monkeys of Japan,* the writer feels he has proved that monkeys are not ruled by instinct.
- The writer of *Monkey Behaviour* thinks that all animals and insects are purely ruled by instinct.
- The writer of *Monkey Behaviour* believes that only humans are not purely ruled by instinct.

Section Four — Reading Practice Questions

Page 23 — Practice Questions

Q1
- rounded bodies
- new and ghastly looking creatures
- in shape somewhat resembling an octopus
- with huge and very long and flexible tentacles
- The skin had a glistening texture, unpleasant to see, like shiny leather
- tentacle-surrounded mouth
- They were the size of a fair-sized swine
- the tentacles seemed to him to be many feet in length

Q2

Any picture that looks a bit like this is fine.

Q3 ii) The skin had a glistening texture, unpleasant to see, like shiny leather.

Q4
- it does not appear that Mr Fison was afraid, or that he realised that he was in any danger
- his confidence is to be ascribed to the limpness of their attitudes
- he was horrified, of course, and intensely excited and indignant

Q5
- large intelligent eyes
- their eyes regarded him with evil interest
- making a soft purring sound to each other

Q6
- moved to and fro
- emerging from the sea
- The rounded bodies fell apart
- slowly uncoiling their tentacles, they all began moving towards him
- creeping at first deliberately

Q7 iii) Very slowly — Builds up suspense

Q8 *Your answer could include the following points:*
- The writer describes the creatures as "ghastly looking".
- The writer uses the simile that the creatures' skin had a "glistening texture, unpleasant to see, like shiny leather", which makes them sound very ugly.
- The creatures move slowly, which builds up suspense and makes the creatures seem more menacing.
- The writer says that Mr Fison is "horrified" at seeing the creatures.

Answers

- The writer uses personification in phrases like "their eyes regarded him with evil interest" to show that the creatures are intelligent, which makes them seem more horrific.

Page 25 — Practice Questions

Q1 *Any reasonable answer, for example:*
- a mist of tears
- made each delicate fibre of his nature quiver

Q2 Because Dorian hasn't said anything.

Q3 *Any reasonable answer, for example:*
- I would give everything!
- there is nothing in the whole world I would not give!

Q4 Wilde writes that "a sharp pang of pain struck like a knife across him", and this **simile** shows that Dorian feels physically hurt when he realises that he will grow old. Then Dorian **panics** when Wilde writes that "he felt as if a hand of ice had been laid upon his heart".

Q5
- What does Hallward say to Dorian?
- How does Hallward feel about the painting?
- What does Lord Henry say to Dorian?

Q6
- The first two prompts ask how Lord Henry and Hallward feel about each other, but the question asks about how they feel about **Dorian**.
- The third prompt asks about what Dorian thinks about the painting, but the question asks about how **Lord Henry** and **Basil Hallward** act.

Q7 *Any three reasonable prompts, for example:*
- How does Dorian feel about old age at the beginning of the extract?
- Does Dorian's opinion of old age change?
- What does Dorian say about old age at the end of the extract?

Page 26 — Practice Questions

Q8 i) Dorian isn't really aware of his beauty and doesn't believe the compliments he gets.

Q9 *Any reasonable answers, for example:*
- The sense of his own beauty came on him like a revelation.
- Basil Hallward's compliments had seemed to him to be merely the charming exaggerations of friendship.
- He had listened to them, laughed at them, forgotten them.
- They had not influenced his nature.

- the full reality of the description flashed across him

Q10 He sees a painting of himself, by Hallward.

Q11 ii) Dorian realises that he is as beautiful as people have been telling him.

Q12 *Any reasonable answer, for example:* "The sense of his own beauty came on him like a revelation."

Q13 Dorian imagines when his face will be "wrinkled and wizen" and he feels so horrified that the thought hurts "like a **knife** across him". He imagines when "the scarlet would pass away from his lips", which shows that he thinks he will become **ugly**.

Q14 *Any reasonable answer, for example:* Dorian wishes that the portrait could grow old instead of him, so that he can always stay the same age. This tells us that he feels that his appearance is very important.

Q15 *Any three reasonable prompts, for example:*
- How does Dorian feel about himself at the start of the extract?
- What happens to make Dorian change his opinion of himself?
- How does Dorian feel about his appearance afterwards?
- How does Dorian feel about growing old?
- What does Dorian wish for at the end of the extract?

Q16 *Your answer could include the following points:*
- At the beginning of the extract Dorian doesn't believe anyone who says that he is beautiful.
- Dorian's opinion of himself changes as soon as he sees the portrait of himself.
- When Dorian sees the portrait, he realises that he is as beautiful as people have said.
- Dorian imagines when he will be old, and hates the idea of becoming ugly.
- At the end of the extract Dorian wishes that he will never grow old and that the painting could age instead.

Answers

Page 29 — Practice Questions

Q1 Uruguay

Q2

Description of fact	Number
Year of first World Cup Final	1930
Largest stadium audience	200,000
Year Football Association was created	1863
Total viewing figures of 2010 World Cup	3.2 billion
Year Charles Miller took football to Brazil	1894
Number of teams that played in first World Cup	13
Year World Cup match helped to start a war	1969

Q3 China — 5000 years ago

Q4 El Salvador and Honduras

Q5 Jules Rimet

Q6 Paris

Q7 It's a joke: the history actually goes back a very long time — about 5000 years.

Q8 *Any reasonable answer, for example:*
- The simile makes the fans sound crazy.
- To make the fans sound like a big pack of fierce animals.

Q9 *Any reasonable answer, for example:*
- The metaphor makes the football games sound like battles.
- It makes it sound as if there are no rules and people might get hurt.

Q10 *Any reasonable answer, for example:*
- To show that there are three separate ideas about why football is popular.
- To make it easy to follow the text.

Q11 *Any reasonable answer, for example:*
- To make the reader feel like it's a conversation between themselves and the writer.
- To show what each paragraph is about, and the question that each paragraph addresses.

Page 30 — Practice Questions

Q12 *Any reasonable answer, for example:*
- It doesn't explain that the text is about the World Cup until the end of the first paragraph, which encourages the reader to keep reading to find out what's going on.
- The first paragraph starts by putting the reader in the middle of the action, which is quite exciting.
- The writer uses a simile ("snarling like hyenas") to make the description exciting.
- The writer uses interesting imagery
- The writer uses humour in the phrase "it's even more serious — it's the World Cup", which might entertain the reader

Q13

Subsection	Summary
Introduction	Tells you what the article is about and the first World Cup
'Where did football come from?'	The origins of football and how the rules were formed
'Is it really the beautiful game?'	The negative aspects of football
'What's so great about football?'	The popularity of football and the reasons why it is popular
'Who are the biggest football fans?'	The most football-mad fans and the 2010 World Cup

Q14 *Any reasonable summary, for example:*
The article explains the history of football and the World Cup. It describes some good and bad things that football has caused. It tries to explain why it is so popular and finishes by discussing the 2010 World Cup.

Q15 *Any reasonable answer, for example:*
- it hasn't all been good
- these idiots continue to spoil the game for many other people

Q16 He brought two footballs to Brazil

Q17 *Any reasonable answers, for example:*
- A game called calcio was played in Italy in the 16th century, where a decapitated head was used for a ball.
- In medieval Britain football was more like a "bloody, sweaty battlefield", than the game we know today.
- In 1969 a game of football between El Salvador and Honduras contributed to a war between the two countries.

Q18 *Any reasonable answers, for example:*
- The rules are simple.
- It doesn't take much organising to start a game.
- There are often very dramatic incidents in games.

Q19 *Any reasonable answer, for example:*
- The ending talks about something the reader will probably know about — the 2010 World Cup.
- The writer talks about themselves, saying that they also got caught up in the excitement — this makes the ending more personal.
- The article ends with a bit of humour, when the writer says that they still doesn't understand the offside rule.

Answers

Q20 *Any reasonable answer, for example:*
- The writer thinks that football is exciting (they compare a match to a scene from *Braveheart* in the first paragraph).
- The writer knows that football is popular — they say it's the "game we know and love".
- The writer doesn't like people spoiling football — they call football hooligans "idiots".
- The writer says that they got caught up in the national excitement surrounding the 2010 World Cup.
- They don't really understand football completely — they say they don't understand the offside rule.

Q21 *Any reasonable answer, for example:*
- The writer says that the World Cup is more serious than *Braveheart* in the first paragraph, which makes it sound a lot more important than it really is.
- The writer says that "The history of football goes back ever so slightly further than 1930", which is funny because football is about 5000 years old. This makes the reader realise that the article isn't just about dry facts and figures.
- The writer compares medieval football to a battlefield, which is funny because it shows the reader how different football used to be.
- The article ends with humour, when the writer says that they still don't understand the offside rule — this makes the reader laugh at the end of the article and shows that the article was supposed to be fun.

Q22 *Any reasonable answers, for example:*
- The writer shows that football can be scary in the first paragraph, when they compare football fans to snarling hyenas
- The writer shows that the history of football hasn't been all nice, such as the Italians using a head as a ball
- The writer implies that Charles Miller introducing football to Brazil was a good thing, because now Brazil is "the home of the most beautifully-played football in the world"
- The writer says that football hooligans "spoil the game", and they call them "idiots"
- The writer says that even they got caught up in the national excitement, and they seem to believe that it's good that everyone gets excited about the same thing

Section Five — Shakespeare

Page 31 — Know Your Play

Q1 *Answers to this question will depend on what play you're studying. Here are examples for 'Romeo and Juliet' and 'The Tempest'.*

<u>Romeo and Juliet</u>

Act 1 — The Montague and Capulet families hate each other. Romeo is lovesick because the girl he loves, Rosaline, doesn't love him back. Romeo meets Juliet for the first time at the Capulets' party and falls in love with her straightaway.

Act 2 — Romeo breaks into the Capulets' mansion and finds out that Juliet loves him. They declare their love for each other. At the end of the act they get married.

Act 3 — Mercutio is killed by Tybalt, so Romeo kills Tybalt in revenge. Romeo is exiled but says that he would rather die. Juliet is told that she has to marry Paris.

Act 4 — Juliet says she would rather die than marry Paris. Friar Lawrence hatches a plan so that Juliet can fake her own death, then escape to be with Romeo. Juliet pretends to want to marry Paris, but then takes a sleeping potion to make herself appear dead.

Act 5 — Romeo hears that Juliet is dead. He rushes back to Verona with a plan to poison himself. Friar Lawrence had sent a letter to Romeo telling him about the plan, but it never arrived. When Romeo reaches Juliet's tomb, Paris tries to stop him getting in, so Romeo kills him. Romeo poisons himself and dies. Juliet wakes up just as Friar Lawrence arrives, sees that Romeo is dead and kills herself to die with him. Everyone arrives and Friar Lawrence tells them all what happened. The Capulets and Montagues give up their feud.

<u>The Tempest</u>

Act 1 — Alonso and his followers are caught in a storm and washed up on a remote island. Prospero tells Miranda that Alonso and Antonio betrayed him in the past, and Miranda and Ferdinand fall in love.

Act 2 — Antonio and Sebastian plot to kill Alonso. Trinculo, Caliban and Stephano meet.

Act 3 — Miranda and Ferdinand agree to marry, and Caliban persuades Stephano to kill Prospero. Ariel plays a magic trick on Alonso and his followers.

Answers

Act 4 — Prospero says Miranda and Ferdinand can get married, then goes off to deal with Caliban, Stephano and Trinculo.

Act 5 — Prospero forgives his enemies and gives up his magic. The characters prepare to set off home.

Q2 *Answers to this question will depend on what play you're studying. Here are examples for 'Romeo and Juliet' and 'The Tempest'.*
Romeo and Juliet

Act 1 Scene 1 — There is a huge fight between the Montagues and Capulets. The Prince warns everyone that he's had enough of the fighting. Romeo comes in and complains about his love for Rosaline.

Act 1 Scene 2 — Paris tries to persuade Lord Capulet to let him marry Juliet. Lord Capulet says it's OK with him but it's up to Juliet. Romeo, Mercutio and Benvolio find out about the Capulet party and decide to gatecrash.

Act 1 Scene 3 — Lady Capulet tells Juliet that Paris wants to marry her, then they go to the Capulet party.

Act 1 Scene 4 — Romeo, Mercutio and Benvolio head to Capulet's party. Romeo worries about a dream he's had, and Mercutio makes fun of him.

Act 1 Scene 5 — At the party, Romeo meets Juliet and they fall in love. Tybalt is angry with Romeo for gatecrashing.

Act 2 Scene 1 — After the party, Romeo decides to break into the Capulet house so he can see Juliet again.

Act 2 Scene 2 — Romeo goes to talk to Juliet at her balcony. They say they love each other.

Act 2 Scene 3 — Romeo talks to Friar Lawrence, and convinces him that he loves Juliet. He says Rosaline, his old crush, is history.

Act 2 Scene 4 — Romeo, Benvolio and Mercutio are joking around. The Nurse comes with a message from Juliet. Romeo tells the Nurse that he loves Juliet.

Act 2 Scene 5 — The Nurse tells Juliet that Romeo loves her, and he has arranged for them to get married that afternoon.

Act 2 Scene 6 — Friar Lawrence is convinced that Romeo and Juliet should get married, so he marries them straightaway.

Act 3 Scene 1 — Tybalt tries to fight Romeo. Romeo refuses because he doesn't want to fight Juliet's cousin, so Mercutio fights instead and is killed. Romeo is so angry that he kills Tybalt. As a punishment, the Prince exiles him.

Act 3 Scene 2 — Juliet finds out that Romeo killed Tybalt and has been banished. She doesn't know if she should be upset that Romeo killed Tybalt, upset that Romeo is banished, or glad that Tybalt didn't kill Romeo.

Act 3 Scene 3 — Romeo finds out he has been exiled, but says he would rather die than live without Juliet.

Act 3 Scene 4 — Lord Capulet secretly arranges for Juliet to get married to Paris.

Act 3 Scene 5 — Romeo goes to say goodbye to Juliet. Lady Capulet comes and tells Juliet she is going to marry Paris. Juliet refuses and Lord Capulet gets angry.

Act 4 Scene 1 — Juliet tells Friar Lawrence that she would rather die than marry Paris, so he hatches a plan for her to fake her own death by taking a sleeping potion.

Act 4 Scene 2 — Juliet goes home and pretends she wants to marry Paris.

Act 4 Scene 3 — Juliet takes a sleeping potion to make her appear dead.

Act 4 Scene 4 — Lord and Lady Capulet prepare for the wedding.

Act 4 Scene 5 — On the day of the wedding, Juliet appears to have died. Everyone is devastated, and the wedding becomes a funeral.

Act 5 Scene 1 — Romeo hears that Juliet is dead. He buys some poison and heads back to Verona.

Act 5 Scene 2 — Friar Lawrence realises that a letter he sent to Romeo telling him that Juliet wasn't really dead has not been delivered, so he sets off to break Juliet out of the tomb when she wakes up.

Act 5 Scene 3 — Romeo is about to break into Juliet's tomb, when Paris spots him. They fight and Romeo kills Paris. Romeo finds Juliet and takes the poison so he can die with her. Juliet wakes up, sees that Romeo is dead, and stabs herself. Friar Lawrence arrives too late. The watch arrive and the whole story is revealed.

Answers

The Tempest

Act 1 Scene 1 — The ship carrying Alonso and his followers is caught in a violent storm.

Act 1 Scene 2 — On the island, Prospero, who raised the storm with his magic, tells Miranda that, in the past, Antonio and Alonso robbed him of his title of Duke of Milan. Prospero and Miranda were then set adrift at sea, with only Gonzalo helping them. Ferdinand arrives and he and Miranda fall in love straightaway, but Prospero decides to test their love and make things difficult for them.

Act 2 Scene 1 — Alonso believes Ferdinand must have drowned in the storm. Antonio persuades Sebastian to kill Alonso while he is sleeping, so that Sebastian can become King of Naples, but Ariel arrives just in time to stop them.

Act 2 Scene 2 — Trinculo meets Caliban when he tries to take shelter under Caliban's cloak. Stephano, who is drunk, finds them and gives Caliban some wine, and Caliban thinks Stephano must be a god.

Act 3 Scene 1 — Miranda comforts Ferdinand as he piles up logs as ordered by Prospero. Miranda and Ferdinand agree to get married.

Act 3 Scene 2 — Stephano, Trinculo and Caliban are all drunk, and Stephano beats up Trinculo when Ariel makes it seem that Trinculo is calling him a liar. Caliban tells Stephano that, if he kills Prospero, Stephano can have Miranda and be 'King of the island'. Stephano agrees to do it.

Act 3 Scene 3 — Ariel makes a magic banquet appear in front of Alonso and his followers, before making it suddenly vanish. He also tells them that the shipwreck was their punishment for throwing Prospero out of Milan. Alonso is sure Ferdinand is dead, and Gonzalo tries to keep everyone calm.

Act 4 Scene 1 — Prospero says Ferdinand and Miranda can get married and they watch some spirits perform a masque to celebrate. Then Prospero suddenly remembers the plot to kill him, and Prospero and Ariel chase off Caliban, Stephano and Trinculo.

Act 5 Scene 1 — Prospero casts a final spell on Alonso and his followers before forgiving them all, and revealing that Ferdinand is alive and engaged to Miranda. The Boatswain arrives and says the ship is fine, and Prospero invites them all back to his cave before they set off home. Stephano, Trinculo and Caliban get told off, and are ordered to tidy Prospero's cave. Ariel is set free once he's arranged good weather for the journey.

Epilogue — Prospero asks for the audience's support on his journey back to Milan.

Q3, Q4, Q5, Q6 *Answers to these questions depend on which play you're studying.*

Q7 a) A big section of a play
b) A shorter section of a play — part of an act
c) One of the people in the play
d) A play where people die at the end
e) A play where people get married at the end
f) A play based on real history
g) Dialogue that's not poetry — normal speech
h) Dialogue in separate lines with a rhythm
i) The rhythm of poetry
j) When one character leaves the stage
k) When more than one person leaves the stage
l) When a character says something to the audience that the other characters can't hear

Page 32 — Understanding the Language

Q1 thy — your
ere — before
thee — you
thou wilt — you will
hither — to here
he hath — he has
hie — go
thou art — you are
thou hast — you have
wherefore — why
hence — from here
thou — you

Q2 a) conjurations — stories / illusions
felon — criminal
b) outstrip — be better than, surpass
c) saucy — rude
scathe — injure
contrary — contradict
d) prosper — are successful
Tunis — Tunisia (a place)
paragon — perfect example

96

Answers

Page 33 — Understanding the Language

Q3 *Any reasonable answer, for example*:
ALONSO I don't want to hear this. I wish I had never let my daughter get married there (in Tunis), because on the journey I have lost my son, and at the same time my daughter is so far away from Italy that I'll probably never see her again. Oh my son, and heir of Naples and Milan, I wonder which fish ate you when you drowned.

Q4 *Any reasonable answer, for example*:
ROMEO You can't talk about something you have no experience of. If you were my age, and had gone through everything I have, then you could say what you think. Then you might also tear out your hair and roll around the ground like I do, wishing you were dead.

Q5 *Any reasonable answer, for example*:
PROSPERO Look, it's me, Prospero — the man who was Duke of Milan but had it stolen from him. If you need more proof that it's me, I'm going to hug you, and warmly welcome you and your friends.

Q6 *This answer depends on which play you're studying.*

Page 34 — Backing Up Your Answers

Q1 **a)** "good Capulet, which name I tender / As dearly as mine own"
b) • "if ye should lead her into a fool's paradise, as they say, it were a very gross kind of behaviour"
• "if you should deal double with her, truly it were an ill thing to be offered to any gentlewoman, and very weak dealing"
c) "most wicked sir, whom to call brother / Would even infect my mouth, I do forgive"
d) "Shall I speak ill of him that is my husband?"
e) • "moonshine"
• "green sour ringlets"
• "the ewe"
• "midnight mushrooms"
• "noontide sun"
• "mutinous winds"
• "green sea"
• "azured vault"

Page 35 — Backing Up Your Answers

Q2 **a)** • "Thy old groans ring yet in my ancient ears"
• "Lo, here upon thy cheek"

b) • "thou mayst brain him"
• "Batter his skull"
• "paunch him with a stake"
• "cut his wezand with thy knife"
c) "O, the heavens!"
d) "Put not another sin upon my head"

Page 36 — Writing Your Answers

Q1 **a)** Yes
b) "Who wrote hit after hit after hit."
c) If the works were hits then lots of people must have gone to see the plays.
The limerick tells us that Kit's work was very popular — he wrote "hit after hit after hit". The repetition here emphasises that he wrote many successful plays, not just one.

Q2 **a)** • Lords, ladies and gents all rated his skills
• hit after hit after hit
b) Repetition, e.g. "hit after hit after hit"
c) Repetition makes him sound even more popular — "lords, ladies and gents" sounds like all the important people liked Kit and "hit after hit after hit" suggests an unlimited number of hits.
One way in which the writer emphasises Kit's popularity is by using repetition — he wrote "hit after hit after hit". This suggests that people keep coming back to see Kit's plays — even the "Lords, ladies and gents" think he's talented.

Q3 *Any reasonable answer, for example:*
The writer says the geese didn't like Kit because he used the geese's feathers as quills to write his plays — "Each day he used up forty goose-feather quills".

Q4 *Your answer could include the following points:*
• The writer says that the play was like "a grand opera and a fireworks display rolled into one". This makes the play sound extravagant like an opera and spectacular like a fireworks display.
• The fact that the writer says "Luke Matchett lived the role" makes it sound as if he was doing more than acting, and so was very convincing in the role.
• The writer says that Caliban was "suitably evil", but the actor managed to convey an "underlying sadness". The fact that they're describing the actor doing two things at once shows that they're impressed.
• At the end of the review, the writer calls the play "An absolute triumph!" This is quite an over-the-top way of saying the performance was good, so it shows they are really enthusiastic about it.

Answers

Answers

Page 37 — Writing Your Answers

Q5 *Any reasonable answer, for example:*
This extract shows that Romeo and Juliet love each other despite their families being enemies. They are prepared to give up their names in order to be together: "Call me but love, and I'll be new baptised". This shows that their relationship is stronger than their loyalty to their families.

Q6

Point	Quote
Names play an important part in 'Romeo and Juliet'.	"What's in a name?"
Juliet wants Romeo to give up his name.	"doff thy name, and for thy name, which is no part of thee, / Take all myself."
Romeo hates his name.	"My name, dear saint, is hateful to myself, / Because it is an enemy to thee"
Juliet wasn't expecting to hear Romeo.	"What man art thou that thus bescreened in night / So stumblest on my counsel?"

Q7 *Any reasonable answer, for example:*
The atmosphere in this extract is very romantic. Romeo and Juliet talk about abandoning their family ties so that they can be together. The use of poetic language, for example the sweet smelling rose, and "call me but love" give the impression that what we are seeing is true love, which is very romantic.

Page 38 — What Characters Do

Q1 *Any reasonable answers, for example:*
a) Romeo — quick to fall in love, determined
Juliet — desirable, romantic
b) <u>Romeo</u> is quick to fall in love — he falls for Juliet the first time he meets her.
<u>Romeo</u> is very determined — he climbs the Capulets' wall just to see Juliet again.
<u>Juliet</u> is desirable — Paris wants to marry her.
<u>Juliet</u> is romantic — she kisses Romeo at the party, and tells him she loves him when he comes to visit her balcony.

Q2 **a)** "I've thought of a plan, but it's dangerous."
"If you are strong enough to die rather than marry Paris..."
"...then you'd be prepared to face death if it solved your problem."
"If you dare to do it, then I'll help."
b) *Any reasonable answer, for example:*
This extract suggests that Friar Lawrence is a wise and cunning man, as he quickly comes up with a solution to Juliet's problem. He is happy to help Juliet against the wishes of her family — which shows that he is loyal to her and Romeo.

Page 39 — What Characters Say

Q1 **a)** A — Caliban says that he used to be treated better, and that rightfully the island is his.
B — Caliban wants to have a party.
b) A — Caliban says that the island was his mother's, so now he should own it: "This island's mine, by Sycorax my mother".
c) A — Caliban says that the island was his before Prospero took it off him: "thou tak'st from me".

Q2 **a)** A — Prospero talks about how he and Miranda were banished from Milan.
B — Prospero says he forgives Antonio and Sebastian for betraying him and plotting against Alonso.
b) *Any reasonable answers, for example:*
• forgiving
• moral
• victim

Q3 **a)** *Any reasonable answers, for example:*
A — Men who are about to die are often happy.
B — Death has taken your breath, but you still have your beauty, so it hasn't won yet.
b) *Any reasonable answers, for example:*
• eloquent
• romantic
• stubborn

Page 40 — What Characters Say

Q4 **a)** **i)** Alonso is pessimistic. — He feels sure Ferdinand is dead.
ii) Alonso feels guilty. — He blames himself for what's happened to Ferdinand.
iii) Alonso is irritable. — He's annoyed when people try to cheer him up.
b) **i)** • "My son is lost"
• "what strange fish / Hath made his meal on thee?"
ii) "Would I had never / Married my daughter there, for, coming thence, / My son is lost"
iii) "You cram these words into mine ears against / The stomach of my sense."

Q5 **a)** **i)** Juliet has been feeling down recently — "to put thee from thy heaviness"
ii) Juliet's dad has worked hard to get the wedding sorted quickly. — "thou hast a careful father, child, / One who... / Hath sorted out a sudden day of joy"
iii) Juliet is reluctant to marry Paris. — "He shall not make me there a joyful bride"

Answers

Page 41 — What Characters Say

Q6 *Any reasonable answers, for example:*

Point	Quote	Explanation
Romeo is ungrateful for all the luck he's had recently.	"A pack of blessings lights upon thy back."	Friar Lawrence explains that Romeo should be glad to be alive and well.
Romeo has been saved from execution even though he killed Tybalt.	"The law that threatened death becomes thy friend, / And turns it to exile"	As a murderer, Romeo should have been executed.
Romeo wanted to be dead for Juliet's sake.	"Thy Juliet is alive, / For whose dear sake thou wast but lately dead"	Romeo wanted to die rather than be exiled away from Juliet.

Q7 *Any reasonable answers, for example:*

Point	Quote	Explanation
Prospero treats Caliban harshly.	"thou shalt have cramps, / Side-stitches that shall pen thy breath up"	He threatens him with painful punishments.
In the past, Prospero was kind to Caliban.	"wouldst give me / Water with berries in't, and teach me how / To name the bigger light and how the less"	He fed him and taught him about the sun and moon.
Caliban is bitter at Prospero.	"This island's mine by Sycorax my mother, / Which thou tak'st from me."	He says Prospero stole the island from him.

Page 42 — How Characters Think

Q1 a) He tells him to fetch some fuel.
b) Because he doesn't do it straightaway.
c) Because he is scared of the power of Prospero's magic.

Q2 A — ii)
B — iii)
C — i)

Q3 a) • "Thou most lying slave"
• "stripes may move"
• "Filth as thou art"
b) He tried to violate (attack) Miranda.

Page 43 — Writing About Descriptions

Q1 a) • Something big is going to happen tonight.
• The party tonight will end badly.
• God's in charge of my life, he'll do what he wants.
• Let's get going.
b) *Any reasonable answers, for example:*
• "I fear, too early, for my mind misgives / Some consequence yet hanging in the stars"
• "bitterly begin his fearful date / With this night's revels"
c) *Any reasonable answer, for example:*
• "Direct my sail!"
• "Some consequence yet hanging in the stars"
d) He says that God is steering his course and there is nothing he (Romeo) can do about it, so they may as well get going.

e) *The answers a)-d) should be used, in any order, to answer the question.*

Q2 *These are just some of the points you could make in your answer. Don't forget the quotes:*
• The Prince uses several phrases which suggest that the families have fought before; "Rebellious subjects", "enemies to peace".
• The Prince says that they have "thrice disturbed the quiet of our streets" and talks about "Three civil brawls". This suggests that there have been three fights recently.
• The Prince says that Verona's citizens have had to take up weapons to stop the fighting, which suggests that the fighting normally happens in public places, and that it is very serious and violent.
• The Prince has to shout to be heard; "Will they not hear?", which suggests that the fighters are more interested in their fight than the law.

Page 44 — Writing About Imagery

Q1 A:a) Passionate love
b) Explosions / fire and gunpowder
c) It is unpredictable and dangerous.
d) Friar Lawrence is worried about what is going to happen to Romeo and Juliet's relationship in the future.
B:a) Sword fighting
b) Playing a musical instrument
c) It is energetic and can be unpleasant, like badly played music.
d) Mercutio is angry and wants to fight Tybalt, making him dance around, or dodge his sword for insulting him.
C:a) How Caliban, Stephano and Trinculo will be tormented and covered with bruises.
b) Leopards
c) They won't just have a few bruises, they will be completely covered in them.
d) Prospero is determined to punish them for plotting against him.

Q2 *These are just some of the points you could make in your answer. Don't forget the quotes:*
• The phrase "A rotten carcass of a butt" suggests a decaying and dangerous boat, not fit for the Duke of Milan. This would add to the sense that the people who overthrew Prospero were evil and heartless.
• The imagery of the rats leaving the boat gives the impression of even more danger — the little boat wasn't only small and unpleasant but must have been dangerous as well if the rats had abandoned it.

Answers

- Saying that the sea "roared" adds to the tension and danger of the story; the danger that Prospero is describing makes his story even more dramatic.
- The description of the winds as "sighing" and the description of them as taking pity on Prospero gives the impression that the elements were on his side. This adds to the sense of magic in the scene — Prospero must be a really powerful wizard to be able to change and control the weather.

Page 45 — Writing About Mood

Q1 *Any reasonable answers, for example:*

	Setting	How the characters speak	Description and imagery	Mood
A	The Island	They speak in prose, Trinculo and Caliban insult each other a lot.	Trinculo calls Caliban a "monster" and a "natural".	Comical, aggressive
B	Juliet's Room	Juliet is talking to herself. She is speaking in riddles.	"Say thou but 'ay' / And that bare vowel 'I' shall poison more..."	Impatient, tense, panicked
C	Outside the Capulet's House	Mercutio is playing with words and speaking in riddles.	"Romeo! Humours! Madman! Passion! Lover!"	Comical, magical, mystical, over-dramatic

Q2 *Use all the points you made in Q1 and don't forget quotes to back up everything you say.*

Page 46 — Writing About Persuasive Language

Q1 Says it will be very simple to kill Alonso:
- "If he were that which now he's like — that's dead — / Whom I with this obedient steel, three inches of it, / Can lay to bed for ever"

Laughs at the idea of feeling guilty:
- "Twenty consciences / That stand 'twixt me and Milan, candied be they / And melt, ere they molest!"

Says Gonzalo won't be a problem:
- "This ancient morsel, this Sir Prudence, who / Should not upbraid our course."

Says no one else will stand in their way:
- "For all the rest, / They'll take suggestion as a cat laps milk, / They'll tell the clock to any business that / We say befits the hour."

Q2 Stands up to insults:
- "Blistered be thy tongue / For such a wish!"
- "Shall I speak ill of him that is my husband?" (as a comeback to the Nurse's criticism)

Uses violent language to emphasise her emotions:
- "O what a beast I was to chide at him!"
- "Blistered be thy tongue / For such a wish!"

Uses romantic language:
- "He was not born to shame"
- "Sole monarch of the universal earth"
- "'tis a throne where honour may be crowned"

Insists Romeo is honourable:
- "He was not born to shame: / Upon his brow shame is ashamed to sit; / For 'tis a throne where honour may be crowned"

Uses rhetorical questions:
- "Shall I speak ill of him that is my husband?"

Q3 *Whichever one you do, try to make as many points (backed up by quotes) as you can. Use your answers from question 1 or 2 to help you write your answer.*

Page 47 — Performance — The Basics

Q1 "They are both in either's pow'rs, but this swift business / I must uneasy make, lest too light winning / Make the prize light."

Q2 thoughtful, quiet

Q3 forceful, loud, angry, accusatory

Q4 *Any reasonable answer, for example:*

At the start of the extract, Romeo seems calm, but he's quite emotional. He uses phrases such as "Good, gentle youth", which makes Romeo seem gentle, but the phrase "tempt not a desperate man" adds tension to the scene.

Romeo becomes more desperate sounding through the passage, begging Paris to give up and leave; "Put not another sin upon my head, / By urging me to fury".

When Paris refuses to let Romeo pass and tries to arrest him, Romeo instantly loses his temper. He doesn't even give Paris a second chance, but attacks him viciously; "have at thee, boy!". This shows how desperate and emotional Romeo is at the end of the extract.

100

Answers

Page 48 — How Characters Speak

Q1 *Any reasonable answers, for example:*
"Affection makes him false, he speaks not true"
Lady Capulet feels angry because she thinks that the Montagues are lying to defend one another. She could shout these words angrily at the Prince.
"Romeo must not live."
Lady Capulet is determined to get justice — Romeo killed Tybalt, so now Romeo must die. She could say these words assertively to convince the Prince to execute Romeo.
"His fault concludes but what the law should end, / The life of Tybalt."
Montague is desperate because he is trying to convince the Prince that Romeo was right to kill Tybalt and should not be punished. He could say these words pleadingly to the Prince.
"I have an interest in your hearts' proceeding; / My blood for your rude brawls doth lie a-bleeding"
The Prince is upset because he is related to Mercutio, who has been killed. He could say these words sadly or bitterly.
"I will be deaf to pleading and excuses"
The Prince is determined to uphold the law and not be persuaded otherwise. He could say these words firmly and loudly to silence Montague and Lady Capulet.

Q2 *Any reasonable answer, for example:*
- *"O good Gonzalo ... word and deed."*
  He could emphasise his gratitude and good will towards Gonzalo by speaking clearly and slowly.
- *"Most cruelly ... furtherer in the act"*
  He could sound angry and reproachful, to emphasise his bitterness about what Alonso and Sebastian did. He could also sound calm though, as he has had plenty of time to think about what happened.
- *"Thou art pinched for't now, Sebastian."*
  Prospero could raise his voice at this point, perhaps emphasising the word "pinched", to show his satisfaction that Sebastian is being punished for what he did.
- *"Flesh and blood ... Unnatural though thou art."*
  Prospero could again sound angry, but also have a disbelieving, incredulous tone, to show he is still shocked and hurt that his own brother could betray him.

- *"Their understanding ... or would know me."*
  Prospero could have a fairly neutral tone for these lines, as he is simply commenting on the fact that his enemies are coming back to their senses after the spell.
- *"Ariel, / Fetch me the hat and rapier in my cell."*
  He could sound slightly more urgent and businesslike at this point, as he is asking Ariel to fetch him his hat and sword.

Page 49 — How Characters Move

Q1
- *"The fringed curtains of thine eyes advance"*
  Prospero could point and Miranda could look in the same direction.
- *"Lord, how it looks about!"*
  Ferdinand could be wandering around, looking for something.

Q2 *Any reasonable ideas, for example:*
- Juliet could hold up Romeo's hand as if she is admiring it when she says "For saints have hands that pilgrims' hands do touch."
- When Romeo says "let lips do what hands do", he could hold Juliet's hand, as if he is going to kiss it, maybe he could even bow down to it to show his devotion to her.
- When Romeo says "move not while my prayer's effect I take", he could hold her face and kiss her, whilst she stays still. Juliet could even look a bit flustered at this point.

Q3 *Any reasonable suggestions, for example:*
- When Prospero says the words "foul conspiracy" he could have a disgusted expression on his face, to show his contempt for Caliban and his fellow plotters.
- When Prospero says "Well done! Avoid", he could turn towards the spirits who have been acting in the masque, and gesture impatiently for them to go away, to show he needs to deal with Caliban as quickly as possible.
- Ferdinand could frown in confusion when he says "This is strange", to emphasise his surprise at Prospero's sudden change in mood.
- Miranda could have a worried expression on her face at seeing him "so distempered", to show she is concerned because Prospero doesn't usually act like this.

Answers

Page 50 — Themes in 'Romeo and Juliet'

Q1 **a, b)** • *"'Tis but thy name that is my enemy"*
Juliet is saying that it is only Romeo's name that makes him her enemy, not himself.

   • *"What's Montague?"*
   Juliet is asking what it means to be a Montague that makes you different from any other person.

   • *"O be some other name!"*
   Juliet is saying that if Romeo had any other surname she could be with him.

   • *"What's in a name?"*
   Juliet is asking why your name should matter when it's who you are and not what you're called that's important.

   • *"doff thy name"*
   Juliet is asking Romeo to abandon his name so that they can be together.

c) Juliet seems to recognise that names mean something, but she does not seem to think that they are that important. They are just words, nothing more.

d) Shakespeare may be suggesting that there is more to a person than their family. Names aren't what make you who you are and shouldn't matter.

Q2 *These are some of the things you could write about:*

   a, b) • *"A gentler judgement vanished from his lips, / Not body's death, but body's banishment."*
   This suggests that Friar Lawrence thinks that being alive, but in exile, is better than being executed.

   • *"Ha, banishment! Be merciful, say 'death'"*
   Romeo thinks that being forced to live in exile is worse than death.

   • *"There is no world without Verona walls, /... And world's exile is death."*
   Romeo is saying that exile is a form of hell, a slow, painful death.

   c) • Friar Lawrence thinks that exile is the best possible outcome for Romeo, because he could have been killed. He tells Romeo that "the world is broad and wide", meaning that there will be new opportunities for Romeo.

• Romeo thinks that life outside of Verona is meaningless because everything he knows and loves is there. Living somewhere else would be like losing his soul — he would rather die and get it over with.

   d) • Shakespeare seems to suggest that some things are worth dying for, and not worth living without (e.g. Juliet).

   • He also seems to be suggesting that there are two kinds of death — physical death and emotional death.

Page 51 — Themes in 'The Tempest'

Q1 **a, b)** • *"the sea, which hath requit it"*
The sea has avenged the betrayal of Prospero by shipwrecking his enemies on the island.

   • *"The pow'rs, delaying, not forgetting, have / Incensed the seas and shores, yea, all the creatures, / Against your peace."*
   Fate is not going to let Alonso and his followers escape punishment for their crimes.

   • *"Thee of thy son, Alonso, / They have bereft, and do pronounce by me / Ling'ring perdition, worse than any death / Can be at once, shall step by step attend / You and your ways"*
   Ariel announces that fate is punishing Alonso by taking his son away from him and leading him into everlasting misery.

   • *"else falls / Upon your heads — is nothing but heart's sorrow, / And a clear life ensuing."*
   Alonso will be left to reflect on his actions, in order to clear his conscience.

c) Ariel is saying that all the problems and disasters that have befallen Alonso since the shipwreck are a direct punishment for how he treated Prospero in the past. He says that fate is ensuring that justice is done.

d) Shakespeare seems to be saying that, no matter how long people escape punishment for their crimes, justice will always be done in the end.

Q2 *Any reasonable answer, for example:*

   • *"Your charm so strongly works 'em / That if you now beheld them your affections / Would become tender."*
   Ariel says that, if Prospero could see how much his enemies are suffering from his spells, he would feel really sorry for them.

Answers

- *"Hast thou, which art but air, a touch, a feeling / Of their afflictions, and shall not myself, / One of their kind, that relish all as sharply, / Passion as they, be kindlier moved than thou art?"*
  Prospero says that, if Ariel, who is only a spirit of the air, can feel sorry for them, then he, as a human being, should feel even more sympathy.

- *"Though with their high wrongs I am struck to th' quick, / Yet with my nobler reason 'gainst my fury / Do I take part. The rarer action is / In virtue than in vengeance."*
  Even though Prospero is still angry about how he was betrayed, he's determined to be reasonable and not be ruled by his bitterness. He says it is more honourable to forgive than to take revenge.

- *"They being penitent, / The sole drift of my purpose doth extend / Not a frown further."*
  Prospero says that, if his enemies are sorry for what they've done, then his plan is complete and he doesn't need to punish them any further.

- Prospero values forgiveness more highly than revenge. He thinks that if people are sorry for their bad deeds, they should be forgiven, and not continually punished.

- Shakespeare shows that it is possible to forgive your enemies, no matter how badly they have treated you in the past.

- He suggests that the noblest thing to do is to forgive, rather than take revenge.

Page 52 — Themes

Q1 a), b) • *"Draw, if you be men. Gregory, remember thy washing blow."*
Sampson is encouraging the Montagues to fight with him. He says that they're cowards if they won't draw their swords. He gives Gregory instructions to fight well — to remember his slashing blow. This also serves as a threat to the Capulets, as it shows that Gregory is a good fighter.

- *"What, art thou drawn among these heartless hinds? / Turn thee, Benvolio, look upon thy death."*
  Tybalt is insulting the Montagues.
  He uses alliteration ("heartless hinds") to emphasise what he's saying.
  He threatens to kill Benvolio because Benvolio has his sword drawn.

- *"I do but keep the peace. Put up thy sword, / Or manage it to part these men with me."*
  This shows that not everybody wants to keep the feud going — Benvolio is trying to stop the two sides from fighting. He tells Tybalt that he's trying to keep them apart, and asks him to either put his sword down, or use it to help keep the peace.

- *"As I hate hell, all Montagues, and thee:"*
  Tybalt states clearly that he hates the word peace as much as he hates hell and the Montague family.

- *"Clubs, bills, and partisans! Strike! Beat them down! Down with the Capulets! Down with the Montagues!"*
  One of the citizens is encouraging others to get involved with the fight. He calls for them to grab their weapons. He uses short sentences that make it sound like he's angry and shouting. This shows that the citizens dislike the feuding families.

c) Tybalt is angry because Benvolio has his sword drawn. Tybalt's hatred for the Montagues is shown in the fact that he clearly doesn't trust them — he thinks that Benvolio is threatening him, even though Benvolio says he's trying to stop the others from fighting. Tybalt obviously takes the feud very seriously — he says that he hates the Montagues as much as he hates hell.

d) Shakespeare shows that the feud is very violent and has been going on for a long time — both sides insult each other and are willing to fight. By including the citizens in the fight he shows how the feud is very public, and affects everybody in the city. The fact that the citizen shouts "Down with the Capulets! Down with the Montagues!" shows that the citizens aren't taking sides, but they're angry that the hatred between the two families has been disturbing the peace for such a long time. This emphasises how long the feud has lasted.

Answers

Q2 *Any reasonable answer, for example:*
- *"This island's mine, by Sycorax my mother, / Which thou tak'st from me."*
  Caliban says here that the island belongs to him because it was handed down to him by his mother, Sycorax. He believes Prospero has taken the island from him and claimed power over it.
- *"I loved thee, / And showed thee all the qualities o' th'isle"*
  Caliban says that they were once friends and did not struggle for power. Prospero looked after Caliban, and in return Caliban showed Prospero how to survive on the island.
- *"...and here you sty me"*
  Now Prospero keeps Caliban shut up in a cave like a prisoner.
- *"lying slave, / Whom stripes may move, not kindness!"*
  Prospero calls Caliban a slave who can only be controlled with a whip.
- *"I have used thee, / Filth as thou art, with human care, and lodged thee / In mine own cell"*
  Prospero insists that he has treated Caliban with human kindness and taken him into his home. He doesn't seem to think that there is anything unnatural about their relationship as master and slave.
- Caliban feels used and unfairly treated. He used to be King of his own island. He has seen what it is like to have power and what it is like to live as someone's slave. As a result he challenges Prospero.
- Prospero thinks that he is naturally superior to Caliban, who he doesn't even think is human. He says that he has treated Caliban with respect and tries to put him back in his place as a servant. Prospero refuses to give up his position of authority.
- Shakespeare is maybe suggesting that power, like magic, is an illusion. Prospero seems to be powerful, but there are limits to his powers. His rule is limited to the island, and when he was Duke of Milan he was overthrown.

Section Six — Writing — The Basics

Page 53 — Planning Your Answer

Q1 The correct order is: **vii, ii, vi, iii, i, v, iv**

Q2, Q3 *Any reasonable answers, for example:*
1) A summary of what has happened: A break in at the Bear family home. The Bears returned to their house to find an intruder.
2) First they realise their porridge has been eaten.
3) Then they see that the furniture is out of place.
4) Finally they spot a girl sleeping in Baby Bear's bed.
5) When they go to confront the intruder, she wakes up and runs away.
6) Police are warning all bears to lock their doors and remain vigilant.
7) Anyone who may have information on the blonde suspect are asked to contact the police.

Q4 *Any reasonable answer, written in clear paragraphs, using the list and order from Q2 and Q3.*

Page 54 — Writing Essays

Q1 i) There is no introduction.
ii) It doesn't explain who the band are, or give any other context.
iii) It just trails off without a conclusion.

Q2 i) My favourite heavy metal band, "Orange Hamster" (formed in 1989), are as popular today as they ever were.
iv) "Grannyknot" are a band that I strongly dislike. They have very little musical talent, and their lead singer is painfully average.
v) My favourite musical genre is 60s rhythm and blues.

Q3 *Any reasonable answer.*

Q4 *Any reasonable answer that includes an introduction, a conclusion and is written in clear paragraphs.*

Answers

Page 55 — Writing Stories

Q1 ii) a gripping opening to the story
iii) an exciting development in the plot
i) a satisfying ending which ties up all the loose ends

Q2 *Any three reasonable answers.*

Q3 *Any reasonable answers, for example:*
b) The soldiers cowered in the damp trenches, fear written all over their faces.
Ears ringing with the sound of explosions, the soldiers took cover in the trenches, scared for their lives.
c) The spaceship hurtled towards the burning planet, spinning out of control.
In the far reaches of a distant galaxy, a lone spaceship was making a dangerous journey towards an unknown planet.
d) She froze, and glanced behind her into the shadows, convinced she had heard footsteps. Suddenly she heard a noise; someone, or something, was following her.
e) Roaring like an express train, the snow charged down the mountainside towards the stricken climbers.
There was nothing the climbers could do as the avalanche, a white wall of doom, came thundering towards them.

Q4 a) They won the battle. — After days of struggle, the exhausted soldiers were finally victorious.
b) They were together again at last. — They were together again at last, but for how long?
c) The storm ended. — The streets were flooded and fallen trees lined the road, but at last it was over.
d) They sailed off into the sunset. — The boat, silhouetted against the sunset, carried the two lovers to their destiny.
e) They never caught the monster. — "You will never defeat me!" cackled the vampire, and vanished into the darkness.
f) The innocent man was released. — He had always insisted that he didn't do it; now, finally, justice had been done.

Page 56 — Writing to Inform, Explain and Advise

Q1 a) Informs. This text is giving the reader facts about deadly plant species.
b) Advises. This text is giving suggestions to help the reader save water at home.
c) Informs. This text is giving the reader facts about a new leisure centre.

d) Explains. This text is explaining to the reader why the school library has been closed.
e) Explains. This text is explaining to the reader why fizzy drinks are bad for their health.
f) Advises. This text is giving suggestions to the reader to help them to avoid catching the flu.

Q2 1) Explain. This text explains to the reader why swimming is the writer's favourite sport.
2) Inform. This text gives lots of facts to inform the reader about the history of swimming.
3) Advise. This text is gives suggestions to the reader about what to do if they are planning to start swimming regularly.

Q3 *Any reasonable answer that explains why the sport you have chosen is your favourite.*

Page 57 — Writing to Inform, Explain and Advise

Q4 i) Pizerrella's Pizzeria first opened its doors in 2003, and has been offering both sit-in and take-away services to local customers ever since.
iii) The pizzeria serves up a wide range of pizzas, including the Vesuvius, with hot chilli, and the Liechtenstein, with frankfurter sausage.
v) Pizarrella's Pizzeria is open from 5 pm to 10.30 pm Monday to Thursday, and 12 noon to 12 midnight Friday to Sunday.

Q5 *Any reasonable answers, for example:*
b) Perhaps you should take part in the race.
c) Maybe you could leave your job.
d) It might be nice to go swimming at the leisure centre tomorrow.
e) You should try to make a decision soon.

Q6 *Any reasonable answer, for example*:
Dear Nat,
It can be tough making friends at a new school, especially if you are a shy person. Although it sounds scary, sometimes going up to people and starting a conversation can be the best way to break the ice. Once people get to know you, they will probably be friendlier towards you. You could also think about joining an after-school club or sports team. This would give you a chance to get to know people with similar hobbies.
Good luck!

Answers

Page 58 — Formal and Informal Letters

Q1

	More formal	Less formal
a)	is not	isn't
b)	was not	wasn't
c)	goodbye	see ya
d)	moreover	what's more, also
e)	children	kids
f)	reprimand	tell off
g)	ensure	make sure
h)	things	stuff
i)	nevertheless	but, however
j)	excellent	fab

Q2 **a)** We would be most interested to hear your thoughts.
b) The competition at this year's sports day is fierce.
c) The number of people owning mobile phones continues to rise.
d) You are requested to contact Ms Pieterson for further details.
e) Customers are advised that SpeedyMart will be closed tomorrow.

Q3 *Any reasonable answer, for example*:

Terrence Tenor
Church Street
Redlington

Wesley West MP
House of Commons
London
Dear Mr. West,

I am writing to insist that you take action against the birds which have settled in the local church.

The pigeons, which started living in the church steeple two months ago, are causing tremendous disruption. For example, they make a lot of noise, distracting people and drowning out the sound of the choir. Also, we have to put up with bird excrement in the choir stalls. It really is too much to bear.

Please agree to address this issue as a matter of urgency.

Yours sincerely,
Terrence Tenor

Page 59 — Formal and Informal Letters

Q4 Dear Mr Brown,
Thank you for your letter.
I am sorry to hear that you **did not** enjoy your meal.
Perhaps you would have enjoyed something from our à la carte menu. **Please find enclosed** a voucher which will **entitle you to** a **complimentary** meal at any of our restaurants.
Yours sincerely,
A. J. Spudwrangler, for Spudwrangler Restaurants.

Q5 *Any reasonable answer, for example:*
Dear Jo,
How are you? I was hoping you could give me some of your good advice. As you know, I've loved doing gymnastics for years and want to keep on doing it.
However, recently I've been stricken with rheumatism which is common among people as old as I am.
Before you retired, I seem to remember you spent some time as a homoeopathist. Do you have any recommendations for herbal remedies which might ease my pain and enable me to backflip again? I do hope you can help.
Lots of love,
Bessie

Q6 *Any reasonable answer, for example:*
Dear Claire,
That video you lent me got me into all sorts of trouble! I took it with me on my last voyage. After I'd learnt the basic moves, I found I was pretty good at it. The music was so infectiously jolly and toe-tapping. Unfortunately, it reached the point where I was finding it really difficult to steer the boat, because I was so busy dancing. I guess you could almost call it an addiction.
Well, all was not lost, as what should I find under a life jacket but my favourite Mozart CD. That CD saved me — I was so relieved to listen to something calm and classical. Finally, three months later than expected, here I am back home. Hope to see you soon dear — but you'd better not lend me any more DVDs!
Best wishes,
Dad

Answers

Page 60 — Writing to Persuade and Argue

Q1 i) Keep your writing polite. Don't intentionally offend people who disagree with your views.

iii) Use descriptive words to emphasise your points.

iv) Get the reader on side by saying "us" and "we".

Q2 a) People need to think about the effect smoking has on their health.

b) The only question we have to ask is, "If the government really has evidence about why we should eat spinach, why don't they tell us what it is?"

c) If you don't want to go on the trip, you must ask your mother to write a letter to the teacher explaining why.

Q3 *Any reasonable answers, for example:*

a) I enjoy swimming because it is relaxing, fun and healthy.

b) It's important to read the newspapers because they are thought-provoking, informative and interesting.

c) We all know that homework is fascinating, inspiring and exciting.

Q4 a) <u>How can you</u> allow these <u>poor, desperate</u> people to go without food <u>any longer?</u>

b) Some people <u>are living</u> in a <u>fantasy world</u> and don't know how normal people live. They <u>seem to think</u> that everyone has enough money to spend on whatever they please.

c) Their team is <u>disorganised</u>, <u>unmotivated</u> and <u>unprepared</u>.

d) If <u>you love</u> theme parks as much as we do, we know that you'll have <u>the time of your life</u> here at Dizzyworld — <u>you'll never want to leave!</u>

Page 61— Writing to Persuade and Argue

Q5 a) Paragraph (a) is not persuasive because it offers a fairly balanced view of the two candidates. It gives good points of both Claire Harris and Edward Jones.

b) Paragraph (b) is persuasive because it tries to persuade the reader that Claire Harris is the better candidate. It describes three of her good qualities for emphasis — that she is "intelligent, honest and cares about the local area." Her policies are praised, while in comparison her rival Edward Jones's track record is criticised.

Q6 a) *Any reasonable answer, for example:*
The death penalty should not be reintroduced in Britain:

There have been several recent cases in Britain where long-serving prisoners have been found innocent because of new evidence. If we had the death penalty in Britain these people would have been wrongly executed long ago.

Lord Justice Hodgeman has said on this issue, "Although I have great faith in the British legal system, we should not lie to ourselves that it is perfect."

b) *Any reasonable answer, for example:*
The death penalty should be reintroduced in Britain:

Keeping people in prison costs the government money — on buildings, staff, food and healthcare. People who have committed horrific crimes and are sentenced to life imprisonment are wasting government resources.

Reintroducing the death penalty would also act as a deterrent to criminals. It would show them that the legal system in Britain is strong and it won't let them get away lightly with their crimes.

Q7 *Any reasonable answer, for example:*
Against cars:

Despite protests from some parents and teachers, cars are still allowed in our school playground. This is a terrible hazard and we need to ask ourselves how much longer it can be allowed to continue.

The strongest argument against cars being allowed in the playground is that they are dangerous. Children run around in the playground, and the risk of an accident is high. There are several examples of children being run over and killed in school playgrounds. These tragedies are horrendous for the schools and families, and an appalling thing for other children to witness.

Some people argue that by driving slowly they can avoid having an accident. This is a misguided attitude. People are often killed or badly injured by cars driving as slowly as 20 mph.

Answers

Another important reason for wanting to keep cars out of the playground is that they take up a lot of space. The playground is a useful area for children to run around, socialise and exercise. If they are kept in a small area of the playground, then their breaktimes will be less healthy and stimulating.

Cars also increase the noise outside the school. This can be distracting for students during lessons, especially during tests.

In conclusion, teachers and parents who complain that there is no other space to park, or that their cars aren't safe elsewhere, aren't thinking about the safety and health of the children they claim to care for. We must support the campaign to keep cars out of the playground for good.

Page 62 — Structuring Your Writing — Introductions

Q1 **ii)** Good evening
iv) We are here tonight to discuss
viii) Welcome
ix) In conclusion
x) The key issue I am going to discuss is

Q2 Paragraph **i)** is more persuasive. It argues clearly in favour of more security in schools. Paragraph **ii)**, on the other hand, describes different points of view as if they are equally valid — this isn't appropriate for a persuasive essay.

Q3 *Any reasonable answer, for example:*
Bob was feeling happy. He had a date with Karen tonight down at the Jammin' Jive Club — it was the over-50s disco night so they could have two games for the price of one. He turned on some Tom Jones, and opened the wardrobe to find his favourite shirt. He blinked; he gulped. All his clothes were torn to shreds. Then, downstairs, he heard a noise. He began to jive his way nervously down the stairs.

Q4 *Any reasonable answer, for example:*
The introduction does not use very persuasive or exciting language. It does not grab the reader's attention and make them want to hear more about the book. It doesn't set up any kind of structure for the rest of the essay.

Page 63 — Structuring Your Writing — Introductions

Q5 Introduction **ii)** signposts clearly what the structure of the leaflet is going to be. It says specifically which three areas are going to be covered by the leaflet.

Q6 **ii)** The second half of this essay will discuss the disadvantages...
iv) There are three main issues at stake here; they will be discussed in turn.
v) The first half of this essay will discuss the advantages...
vi) The second reason for supporting this point of view...
vii) Finally, this essay will consider the impact on...

Q7 *Any reasonable answer, for example:*
The Lake District is one my favourite places to go on holiday for three main reasons. Firstly, it has stunning scenery, including England's biggest lakes and mountains. Secondly, there are a range of fun outdoors activities to take part in, including hiking, kayaking and climbing. Finally, if the weather is poor, there are still plenty of fun things to do, such as paying a visit to the animal park, the aquarium or Keswick's famous pencil museum.

Page 64 — Structuring Your Writing — The Middle Bit

Q1 **v)** Introduction — outline your main argument.
i) Give a reason to support your argument. Back it up with evidence.
vi) Give a second reason to support your argument. Back it up with evidence.
iii) Give a reason why people might not agree with your argument. Give evidence of why they are wrong.
iv) Give a second reason why people might not agree with your argument. Give evidence of why they are wrong.
ii) Conclusion — bring together main points why your argument's right.

Q2 *Any reasonable answer, for example:*
Paragraph 1: The most important reason we need to do more sport in school is because of its proven health benefits. Exercise reduces stress, prevents obesity and keeps the heart strong and healthy.

Answers

Paragraph 2: In addition to health benefits, sport also helps people to develop team skills, which can then be applied in other areas of life.
Paragraph 3: Finally, sports should be played more in school because there is such a wide range of sports to choose from — there is bound to be something everyone can enjoy.

Q3 ii), iii), i), iv)

Page 65 — Structuring Your Writing — The Middle Bit

Q4 a) • The championships will soon be upon us.
• Hard work will be rewarded with good performances.
• Athletes who don't work hard will regret it later.

b) *Any reasonable answer, for example:*
The Championships Will Soon Be Upon Us
• The championships will be over in a couple of weeks.
• The training period will not last long.
All Your Hard Work Will Be Rewarded With Good Performances
• Hard work is the only way to guarantee good performances.
• It will make you feel a sense of achievement when you perform well.
Athletes Who Don't Work Hard Will Regret It Later
• If you don't work hard, you won't perform well.
• You will feel foolish when you do badly.

Q5 *Any reasonable answers, for example:*
a) Arguments for reducing speed limits
• If a driver runs over a pedestrian when he's doing 20 mph, there is a one in five chance they will be killed.
• City speed limits are often as high as 30 mph — the risk to lives is too high.
Arguments against reducing speed limits
• People are often in a hurry, they don't want to go slower.
• Improvements in traffic control and pedestrian crossings make the roads safer, and allow cars to go faster.

b) Arguments for reducing speed limits
• Reducing the number of road deaths is much more important than people's need to travel to places quickly.
• Road accidents can be tragic, and cause a lot of pain and grief.
Arguments against reducing speed limits
• Most drivers are responsible and would slow down if there was a hazard.
• The focus should be on punishing people who break the existing speed limits — they are the drivers who cause accidents. They would still go fast even if you reduced the speed limit.

c) Arguments for reducing speed limits
3) If a driver runs over a pedestrian when he's doing 20 mph, there is a one in five chance the pedestrian will be killed.
4) City speed limits are often as high as 30 mph — the risk to lives is too high.
1) Reducing the number of road deaths is much more important than people's need to travel to places quickly.
2) Road accidents can be tragic, and cause a lot of pain and grief.
Arguments against reducing speed limits
1) Improvements in traffic control and pedestrian crossings make the roads safer, and allow cars to go faster.
2) Most drivers are responsible and would slow down if there was a hazard.
3) The focus should be on punishing people who break the existing speed limits — they are the drivers who cause accidents. They would still go fast even if you reduced the speed limit.

Page 66 — Structuring Your Writing — Conclusions

Q1 This statement is false. The conclusion should bring together the points made in the essay — it shouldn't bring in new information. It's also very important that the conclusion matches the tone and opinion of the rest of the essay.

Q2 **i)** a final statement about the topic
iii) a summary of the main points in your essay
viii) your own view on the topic

Q3 i) — B   ii) — A   iii) — C

Answers

Q4 **a)** This conclusion is too vague, e.g. "destroying the rainforest is probably not a great idea". It doesn't say anything definite or use powerful or persuasive language to clearly get across the writer's viewpoint.

b) This is a good conclusion. It gives the writer's viewpoint and ends on a strong statement. The tone is fairly impersonal and polite.

c) This conclusion is not great because it allows the writer's personal opinion to take over completely. This means that the tone of the writing becomes personal and rude, e.g. "Anyone who doesn't is lazy or selfish".

Page 67 — Structuring Your Writing — Conclusions

Q5 **ii)** tie up all the loose ends in a satisfying way.

Q6 *Any reasonable answer, for example:*
In conclusion, animal testing is cruel and often unnecessary. It causes horrible pain to the animals. In the case of cosmetics testing this seems particularly unnecessary, as they could be tested on humans instead. Although there may be some worth in testing medicines, I still believe it should be kept to a minimum. Any unnecessary testing should be banned.

Q7 *Any reasonable answer, for example:*
Without hesitation, Detective Andersen headed for the recording studio. As he expected, Silvester Smooth's driver was waiting in the lobby, thumbing through a magazine. He showed the driver his shiny police badge.
"I believe your client is holding stolen goods in the boot of his car," the detective said, "I suggest you come with me, and let me reclaim them."
The driver did as he was told, and before long Detective Andersen was cradling Chewy the Chihuahua in his arms. Tomorrow, he would come by again and ask Mr. Smooth some serious questions. For now though, it was time to get Chewy home.

Section Seven — Paragraphs
Page 68 — Paragraphs

Q1 1 — A
2 — D
3 — C
4 — E
5 — B

Q2 Pompeii was a small city of no great importance in the Roman world. One of the few mentions Pompeii gets in ancient texts is in relation to a fight which broke out at the amphitheatre in which several people were killed. We can glean more information from the archaeological excavations at the site. From the size of the site it is estimated that it had about twenty thousand inhabitants. Evidence from the site includes: buildings, the contents of people's houses, wall paintings, graffiti and plaster casts of people who died in the eruption. ___

Q3 As Myrna sat down at the kitchen table, she already felt full. So far she had eaten five blueberry tarts, ten Easter eggs, a rhubarb crumble and 76 fun-size chocolate bars.
Ali ran into the room and saw the last piece of evidence, the double-cream layered pavlova still there on the kitchen table.
"Come on, he's almost here!" he yelled.
"I'm trying," groaned Myrna.
Meanwhile, the dastardly Mr Smiker was walking slowly across the fields, his nose twitching in the breeze. The unmistakable scent of a missing double-cream layered pavlova filled his monstrous nostrils. He smiled a terrifying smile. Even his teeth were evil.

Page 69 — Paragraphs

Q4

P.	Begins	Talks about
1	Most families argue...	basic problem and some solutions
2	If you have satellite...	further problem — satellite TV
3	An alternative to arguing...	alternative solution — don't watch TV
4	To be even more radical...	more radical solution — don't have TV

Q5 Once, when Hilary was at primary school, she'd climbed over the playing field fence. All her friends had run away because they were scared. Hilary had refused to be scared and had started walking as far from school as possible. After about two hours she had reached her own house. Hilary had been annoyed; she'd wanted to have an adventure, not to go home.

Answers

Page 70 — Paragraphs

Q6 We all know that school buses are environmentally friendly. If our school bus was discontinued each child would have to travel to school individually. Seventy-five students make use of the bus service; that's a lot of extra cars. As the headteacher has said, "The pollution caused by the extra cars travelling to school would have a bad effect on the environment."

Q7 **a)** —ii) Rosie couldn't help but be grateful that the weekend had come at last. Joy rose up inside of her as she thought of going to visit her dad on Sunday.

b) —i) "Excuse me, can you tell me where the maternity ward is, please?" Grace asked politely. The hospital receptionist gave her a disapproving look, followed by a reluctant reply.

c) —iii) Beth approached the talent contest like a gladiator ready for battle. She waited confidently in the wings, staring down her fellow performers with an icy look.

Q8 *Any reasonable answers, for example:*
a) I think that we all need to watch what we eat very carefully.
b) I think that you can take quite a relaxed attitude to healthy eating.

Q9 **a)** When choosing a new floor covering, consider the following points:
b) consider the following points:
c) Do you need something that is easily cleaned (a hard floor), or something that is warm and comfortable (a soft carpet)? Don't forget that a hard floor is much noisier and colder than a carpet. Of course, you can have the best of both worlds by using rugs on top of a hard surface.

Page 71 — Linking Paragraphs

Q1 furthermore, another point of view is, with hindsight, a contrasting view is, however, another example of, in addition to this, on the other hand

Q2 *Any reasonable answers, for example:*
A) Nowadays, people know that white lead is dangerous.
B) On the other hand, the view of the Parents' Association on truancy is less strict.
C) However, the views of many parents about cartoons contrast strongly with those of their children.

Q3 *Any reasonable answer, for example:*
When I was ten I lived in Newcastle. It's a big city, and you can get around it by Metro. In the area I lived, called Jesmond, there was a dene (park) you could run around which had a river and a pet's corner.

While I was living in Newcastle, I went to school at 'All Saints' primary school. The school was in temporary accommodation, so most of the classrooms were in portacabins.

Q4 *Any reasonable answer, for example:*
I think that fashion can be as outrageous as you want. What you wear shows what your personality is like. For example, I wear an Acidic Duo hoodie that I got from one of their gigs because it's cool and it shows what music I'm into.

On the other hand, you could look at my parents' idea of fashion. They're really boring and buy clothes from catalogues. They wear their clothes for years. If they buy new clothes they always choose ones identical to what they had before.

Section Eight — Writing Properly

Page 72 — Basic Punctuation and Speech Marks

Q1 **b)** "Anyway, parrots are boring, I was nowhere near them," she said.
d) As they started leading her towards the police van, Holly panicked and shouted, "It was Kate!"

Q2 Jake burst through the door of the garage shop. "Freeze!" he shouted. He was scared; he could feel the sweat rolling down his forehead and flooding his eyes. He moved towards the cashier, holding the bag out in one hand, grasping his water pistol in the other.

"Oh my life!" said the cashier, "Jake Smithson, what are you doing?"

Jake stopped in his tracks. He had been told that a pair of tights over the head would render any human being unrecognisable.

"I'm not Jake Smithson," he said, backing away.

"Yes you are, I used to serve you lunch at St Hilda's Primary School. Fancy that! What are you getting up to these days?" she said. Quietly, she pressed the police alarm under the counter.

Answers

Q3 a) "I'm going home," said Slim, "I've had enough."

b) "My name is Otto," said the stranger, "and I will have my revenge on you all."

c) "I think I'm coming down with the flu," said Anar.
"Oh, I am sorry," said Mark.
"So am I," said Anar.

d) "She was wearing an awful red shirt," said Lena.
"But I think she thought she looked fabulous," said Charlotte.

e) "You must pay me a million pounds!" shouted the robber.

f) "Now then, young man," said the policeman. "What is it officer?" I replied.

Page 73 — Sentences, Phrases and Clauses

Q1 a) no full stop
b) no capital letter at the beginning, no verb
c) no full stop
d) no verb
e) no verb
f) no capital letter at the beginning, no full stop
g) no verb
h) no full stop
i) no verb

Q2 a) phrase
b) phrase
c) clause
d) phrase
e) phrase
f) clause
g) phrase
h) clause
i) phrase

Q3 a) Before the start of term, I'll have to cram in lots of fun.
b) In the Atlantic Ocean, you can see fish swimming.
c) In the new school play, the acting is impressive.
d) Without a bit of mustard, you can't make mustard sauce.
e) Without a doubt, dinosaurs are now extinct.
f) Textbook in hand, my teacher explained it all again.
g) During her latest tantrum, Kim threw an egg against the wall.
h) Up in the attic, my brother has a new bedroom.

Page 74 — Commas, Semicolons and Colons

Q1 a) Walking beside the miniature poodle, Harley felt very tall indeed.
b) I asked her about her holiday, but she ignored me.
c) Scurrying out of the way of the headmistress, Dana looked a bit sheepish.
d) As soon as he saw Frank, the baboon became angry.

Q2 a) The Lake District, which is in northern England, is a popular holiday destination.
b) Not long afterwards, with her hair in a complete mess, my sister returned to the ranch.
c) The weather was far too hot for Bernard, a large bull terrier, as he ran across the park.
d) Stephen, who works with my brother, likes to play golf on the weekend.

Q3 a) I'll tell you how I did it: I walked up to him and asked.
b) All I want from my hamster is: companionship, devotion and a number one single.
c) The show was a disaster: no one remembered their lines and the set collapsed.
d) You should bring the following things: an inflatable dinghy, a life jacket and a foghorn.
e) Tariq was giving up on being a secret agent: he couldn't stop telling everyone about it.

Q4 a) The star required: a trailer with a jacuzzi, preferably at maximum temperature; three servants, including a manicurist; a separate dog kennel, which had to be red; and salmon sandwiches without crusts.
b) The footballer had it all: a strong left foot; a good, well-trained eye for the ball; lightning pace; and nerves of steel.
c) He walked into the room; it was completely dark.
d) Jim had made lots of money; he owned a large percentage of Birmingham.

Page 75 — Apostrophes

Q1 a) It's important to drink lots of water throughout the day.
c) It's sunny outside — why stay indoors?
d) The driver wanted the car repaired because its gearbox was making funny noises.

Q2 a) The ostriches' beaks were all shiny.
b) My brother Alex has got Dad's old car.

Answers

c) She gave him her mum's favourite handkerchief, realising too late that it was covered in snot.

d) The children's section of the menu was uninspiring.

e) Matt's piano was six feet tall; he couldn't reach the pedals.

Q3 a) I **don't** want to trouble you, but your Alsatian is in my garage.

b) The boxer **won't** fight without his lucky rabbit's foot.

c) **Don't** you think it's strange how celebrities get thinner every year?

d) **It's** the best piece of music I have ever heard.

e) It **isn't** that unusual for people to have two part-time jobs.

f) I **can't** go to the gym. I **won't** go to the gym. I **don't** want to go to the gym.

Section Nine — Making It Interesting

Page 76 — Use Different Words

Q1 *Any reasonable answers, for example:*

a) The film I saw this weekend was really **entertaining**. The acting was really **great** which was **impressive** because the characters were quite difficult to get right. I was hoping it would be **enjoyable** because it's based on a really **fantastic** book — one of my favourites, actually. It's a **fine** example of a book that both adults and teenagers can enjoy reading.

b) The most **disgusting** food in the world has to be baked beans. The sauce they come in is **awful**, and the beans taste **weird** too. One of my friends eats baked bean salad, a **gruesome** mixture of cold baked beans and lettuce leaves — it's just **nasty**.

c) It's a bit embarrassing but I find frogs really **frightening**. I don't like the way their **evil** eyes stare at you when you walk past them. But the most **creepy** thing about frogs is probably the noise they make — it **unnerves** me. There's a film coming out next year called 'March of the Frogs', but I think I'll be too **terrified** to go and see it.

Q2 *Any reasonable answers, for example:*

a) drove
b) hurried
c) travelled
d) trudged
e) ambled

Q3 a) "I don't know about you, William, but I think throwing cold porridge at Mr Wimpington is very **disrespectful**."

b) Everyone **admired** Rowan — he was welcoming, loyal and kind.

c) Aron was in trouble for spreading **malicious** rumours about people.

d) Finally, after what seemed like a decade spent looking under her bed, Jen **retrieved** her ski outfit.

e) "It was Emily who did it first!" Assallah **insisted**.

Page 77 — Don't Be Boring

Q1 a) Isabel had only got one ticket. She didn't want to give it away.

b) Pancakes with sugar and lemon are good. Jam filling is also nice.

c) Daria flew over the wall. She landed in a heap at the bottom of the ditch.

d) St Malo is really hot in the summer. You can go swimming in the sea.

e) Una was going to miss the plane. Perhaps she could grab a lift on the boy's skateboard.

Q2 *Any reasonable answer, for example:*
Rita Hayworth was born in 1918 in America. Her original name was Margarita Cansino and her father was Spanish. From a young age she danced in a stage act with her father. She spent a lot of time practising her dancing, which meant she missed out on most of her education. In the late 1930s, she started to get small roles in films. However, the American film industry didn't like the fact that she looked Spanish. Her appearance was therefore changed in the following ways: her black hair was dyed red and her hairline was made higher by electrolysis. In addition to this, her Spanish-sounding name was changed to Rita Hayworth.

Q3 *Any reasonable answers, for example:*

a) The woman was sitting on a bench in the park. After a while she saw a duck coming towards her. She reached into her bag for some bread. Gently, she bent down to feed it to him. Then she spotted her friend walking towards her from across the grass.

b) I love rabbits. My three rabbits are called Eugene, Raymond and Nigel. We play fetch together sometimes. Nigel is my favourite because he can play the piano.

Answers

Q4 *Any reasonable answer, for example:*
Then, just when I thought I was winning —
my old nemesis marched into the room, Miss
Rumple! I was so shocked my entire body went
numb. There was no chance of hiding, so I had
to confront her. I took the catapult from my
pocket, saying to myself, "It's not over until I'm
given double detention for the next six years."

Page 78 — Adjectives

Q1 A <u>glorious</u> day had begun. The <u>powder-blue</u>
sky was dotted with <u>cotton-wool</u> clouds. A
swallow flitted through the <u>still</u> air, her <u>sharp</u>
wings slicing a path effortlessly. Her turns were
<u>swift</u> and <u>precise</u>; she was <u>supreme</u>. Below her,
on the <u>tiny</u> country lanes, <u>red-faced</u> humans
crawled along in their <u>metal</u> coffins, sweating
and sighing their way to the <u>crowded</u> beaches.

Q2 *Any reasonable answer, for example:*
A glorious day had begun. The powder-blue
sky was dotted with cotton-wool clouds. A
little swallow flitted through the still air, her
delicate wings slicing a path effortlessly. Her
turns were **small** and **nimble**; she was **dainty**.
Below her on the tiny country lanes, **monstrous**
humans crawled along in their **giant** coffins,
sweating and sighing their way to the crowded
beaches.

Q3 *Example answers (the nouns have been
underlined and the adjectives are in bold):*
a) The **cautious** <u>boy</u> was scared that the
vicious <u>dog</u> would attack him.
b) The **tiny** <u>mouse</u> began to creep towards the
huge <u>dinosaur</u>.
c) Finally, the **exhausted** <u>woman</u> slumped down
into her **comfortable** <u>armchair</u>.
d) A **gigantic** <u>wave</u> came towards the **little**
<u>shore</u> and drenched the **unsuspecting**
<u>sunbathers</u>.
e) In the **large** <u>park</u> near my **beautiful** <u>house</u>
there is an **ancient** <u>oak tree</u>.
f) I didn't know until that **terrible** <u>moment</u> how
I would cope in such a **challenging** <u>situation</u>.
g) It was three **long** <u>days</u> before they realised
that the **adventurous** <u>hamster</u> had escaped.
h) "It is a **well-known** <u>fact</u> that **gorgeous**
<u>Robert Mitchum</u> was a **brilliant** <u>actor</u>," said
my **infatuated** <u>mum</u>.

Q4 *Any reasonable answers, for example:*
a) Animal testing is cruel and unnecessary.
b) School uniform is unattractive, dull and
annoying.
c) Football is definitely the most popular sport
in the world.
d) Mr Beak's nose was incredibly long.
e) The film was absolutely terrible, particularly
the opening scenes.

Page 79 — Comparing

Q1 *Any reasonable answers, for example:*
a) Ilona turned to the headteacher furiously
and screamed like a **banshee**.
b) As he crept over to the side of the ship,
Levi's shoes squeaked like **mice**.
c) Her face was as red as a **tomato**.
d) The chips looked gorgeous. Henry was as
hungry as a **lion**.
e) The bell rang. Students rushed out into the
corridors like a **stampede**.

Q2 a) It wasn't surprising that Louis won the race.
He was the **fastest** runner in the school.
b) Entering the lion enclosure dressed as a
giant steak was the **worst** idea that Zayn had
come up with so far.
c) "Come on!" shouted Niall. This is the
slowest moving traffic I've ever been in!"
d) Selfish as always, Liam took the **biggest** slice
of pie for himself.
e) Everyone knew that Harry, who had a
lifelong fear of water, was probably the **least**
likely to complete the sponsored swim.

Q3 *Any reasonable answers, for example:*
a) Clare's picture is **more beautiful** than Jessica's.
b) Petar is **more sporty** than Ian.
c) "Oh, Imogen," said Jane, "that is the **best**
cake I've ever tasted."
d) Matthew had always been jealous of Luke
because he was **better** at wrestling.
e) Polina reckoned she was the **cleverest**
member of the family.

Answers

Section Ten — Writing Practice Questions

Page 80 — Practice Questions

Q1 a) ii) a mixture of teachers, pupils and parents
b) "Write an article for your school magazine"

Q2 a) ii) to argue
b) *Any reasonable answer, for example:*
It means that the purpose of the article is to argue in favour of one point of view and to convince the readers that this view is right.

Q3 a) formal, polite
b) It should be fairly formal because it is going to be read by parents and teachers, and is trying to discuss an issue seriously. It should be polite because appearing angry and offensive won't help to convince people that your point of view is right. Teachers and parents are more likely to respond well to a polite, formal style.

Page 81 — Practice Questions

Q4 a) ii) homework is an important issue / I believe that / should pupils be given less homework?
b) Option **i)** has phrases suitable for a speech, not an article.
Option **iii)** is too informal, plus you shouldn't insult people who don't agree with your view.
Option **iv)** is not suitable for a persuasive article because it is too apologetic/not confident enough.
Option **ii)** is best because the style is fairly formal, and the phrases are suitable for a persuasive article.

Q5 *Any reasonable answers, for example:*
a) • Homework makes pupils stressed and tired.
• Homework stops children from taking part in extra curricular activities.
b) • Teachers often set homework from habit, even if it isn't really necessary.
• Teachers often underestimate how long it will take pupils to do homework.

Q6 *Any reasonable answers, for example:*
a) • Homework lets pupils practise skills.
• Homework helps pupils learn information.
b) • Homework helps children learn the skill of working on their own, and managing work in their own time.
• It means revision for exams is easier because the children will have learnt more during the year.

Page 82 — Practice Questions

Q7 a)-c) *Any reasonable answers, for example:*
<u>Reasons you agree/disagree with homework</u>
2. Homework makes pupils stressed and tired.
1. Homework stops children from taking part in extra curricular activities.
• ~~Teachers often set homework from habit, even if it isn't really necessary.~~
3. Teachers often underestimate how long it will take pupils to do homework.
<u>Different opinions people might have about homework</u>
1. Homework lets pupils practise skills.
2. Homework helps pupils learn information.
4. Homework helps children learn the skill of working on their own, and managing work in their own time.
3. It means revision for exams is easier because the children will have learnt more during the year.

Q8 Options **i)** and **ii)** are both good. Option **iii)** isn't very good because it is always necessary to consider both points of view.

Q9 *A good answer will:*
<u>Use the essay plan:</u>
• discuss the points in the essay plan
• give priority to the points that are marked as the most important in the essay plan
• use some of the words and phrases in the 'words and phrases to begin and end your essay' box in the introduction and conclusion.
<u>Structure the essay well:</u>
• clear introduction, middle paragraphs and conclusion
• structured middle section, e.g. points supporting your opinion discussed first, points against your opinion (and why they're wrong) discussed second
<u>Make the essay flow well:</u>
• link paragraphs together smoothly
• signpost the structure for the reader
<u>Use evidence to back up points:</u>
Each paragraph should have a clear point backed up with evidence, e.g. quotes, statistics, examples
<u>Use correct punctuation, spelling and grammar:</u>
• use a variety of punctuation correctly, e.g. question marks, apostrophes, exclamation marks and commas
• punctuate long sentences correctly using commas, semicolons or colons.

Answers

Use interesting vocabulary and sentence structures:
- include some unusual, longer words
- use a variety of verbs
- vary length of sentences
- vary how you start sentences

Use tricks to make the argument more convincing:
- groups of three adjectives
- use "we" and "us"
- be polite

Use a style suitable to the audience / reader:
The article is for readers of the school magazine, including parents and teachers, so it should be fairly formal and polite in style.

Q10, Q11 *No answers for these questions.*

Page 83 — Practice Questions

Q1

Question	Answer
What is the purpose of the piece of writing?	To entertain
Who is going to read it?	Readers of the local Herald newspaper
Write down three words which describe the style of the piece of writing.	*Example answers:* lighthearted, informal, humorous

Q2 a)
- the characters who are mistaken for each other, and why they are so alike
- who mixes them up
- the result of the mix-up

b) *Example answer:*

the characters who are mistaken for each other and why they are so alike
- Shaun and Jason
- They are two brothers from Cheshire who look a bit alike. They're so boring people can't tell them apart.

who mixes them up
A mad professor, called Pete, who's been inventing a new type of witchcraft for three years.

what the result of the mix up is
- Pete meets Shaun. Pete is so bored that he performs a spell to try and make Shaun less boring.
- Jason turns up.
- Pete thinks his spell's gone wrong, and Shaun is becoming more boring. He is so scared that he jumps in the canal.
- Jason and Shaun haul Pete out of the canal.
- They are in the local paper as heroes. No one thinks they're boring anymore.

Q3 *A good answer will:*
Use the essay plan:
use the structure and ideas thought out in the essay plan
Structure the writing well:
- write in paragraphs
- structure your story in an effective way, e.g. introduction, middle bit where something interesting happens, conclusion tying up the loose ends

Make the essay flow well:
link paragraphs together smoothly
Use correct punctuation, spelling and grammar:
- use a variety of punctuation correctly, e.g. question marks, apostrophes, exclamation marks and commas
- punctuate long sentences correctly using commas, semicolons or colons

Use interesting vocabulary and sentence structures:
- include some unusual, longer words
- use a variety of verbs
- vary length of sentences
- vary how you start sentences

Use tricks for good, entertaining writing:
- Build up atmosphere and mood by using description and imagery, e.g. similes and metaphors, adjectives and adverbs, alliteration and onomatopoeia
- Use suspense and surprise to keep the reader interested
- Perhaps write from the point of view of one of the characters in the story
- Avoid using clichés

Use a style suitable to the audience and purpose of the writing:
lighthearted, inoffensive, humorous

Q4 *No answer for this question.*

Page 84 — Practice Questions

Q1-3 *Good answers to these questions will:*
Have completed a rough essay plan:
- For Q1 and Q2 an essay plan based on the planning page provided should have been completed. It should include points made in the question, and your own ideas.
- For Q3 a rough plan should have been sketched out, including points made in the question.

Answers

The writing should use the essay plan:
- discuss the points in the essay plan
- use the structure thought out in the essay plan

Structure the essay well:
- clear introduction, middle paragraphs and conclusion
- structured middle section

Make the essay flow well:
- link paragraphs together smoothly
- signpost the structure for the reader

Use evidence to back up points:
Each paragraph should have a clear point backed up with evidence, e.g. quotes, statistics, examples

Use correct punctuation, spelling and grammar:
- use a variety of punctuation correctly, e.g. question marks, apostrophes, exclamation marks and commas
- punctuate long sentences correctly using commas, semicolons or colons

Use interesting vocabulary and sentence structures:
- include some unusual, longer words
- use a variety of verbs
- vary length of sentences
- vary how you start sentences

Make the writing suitable for the writing purpose:
- Q1 — a piece of informative writing
- Q2 — a piece of writing that advises
- Q3 — a piece of persuasive writing

Use a style suitable to the audience / reader:
- Q1 — readers of a newspaper
- Q2 — pupils at your school
- Q3 — managing director of local theatre